JANUA LINGUARUM

STUDIA MEMORIAE
NICOLAI VAN WIJK DEDICATA

edenda curat

C. H. VAN SCHOONEVELD

Indiana University

Series Minor, 150

PROBABILISTIC PERFORMANCE MODELS OF LANGUAGE

by

RAOUL N. SMITH

UNIVERSITY LIBRARY NOTTINGHAM

1973

MOUTON

THE HAGUE · PARIS

© Copyright 1973 in the Netherlands.
Mouton & Co. N.V., Publishers, The Hague.

*No part of this book may be translated or reproduced in any form,
by print, photoprint, microfilm, or any other means, without written
permission from the publishers.*

LIBRARY OF CONGRESS CATALOG CARD NUMBER: 72-94507

Ce

Printed in Belgium by NICI, Ghent.

PREFACE

There has long been a need for an introductory text on probabilistic models of language. The present text is meant to fill that need by presenting a survey of the highlights of the accomplishments in the field, by introducing new applications and a new model, and by giving the basic tools for expanding on this research.

The field of quantitative linguistics fell into disrepute in the late 1950's as a result of the criticism of generative transformational grammarians. Their criticism, much of it justified, has to be understood, however, within the framework of the competence-performance dichotomy. Hopefully, this book will help to put probabilistic aspects of quantitative linguistics into proper historical perspective and give the reader the chance to accept or reject some of the past and present accomplishments in the field on substantive grounds.

Most of the material has been presented to three groups of graduate students in part of a course on computational linguistics. My thanks are gratefully extended to them for their criticisms and suggestions, especially to Martha Evens and Edward Maxwell. My heartfelt thanks also go to my wife Mary whose encouragement brought this work to fruition and to whom this book is warmly dedicated.

RAOUL N. SMITH
Evanston, Illinois
February, 1972

CONTENTS

1

PROBABILITY

Probability theory is the study of the properties of chance events. A probability is defined as a real number assigned to an event as a measure of its likelihood. Statistics, which is based on the results of probability theory, is the study of inductive inferences about the events and their properties.

That part of probability theory needed to understand concepts developed later in this book deals with repetitive trials of an experiment with a finite number of possible outcomes. Some typical experiments in linguistics involve examining letters or words or morphemes appearing in sequence in a text, determining what rules of the grammar have been applied or what features are present. Possible outcomes from such experiments would be the letter ⟨u⟩ appearing in a text, or the word ⟨sandwich⟩, or the noun plural morpheme {Z}, or the rule $NP \rightarrow N\ S$ being applied, or the feature [+ animate] having occurred.

The first step in choosing an appropriate assignment of probabilities is the determination of the space S of all possible outcomes. For the examples given above this would be all the letters, all the words, all the noun morphemes or all the morphemes, all the NP rules or all the rules of the grammar, all the lexical features. In the example where the space S consists of letters of the alphabet some events are:

the set containing the first five letters of the alphabet
$A = \{a, b, c, d, e\}$

the set of letters commonly representing English voiced stops
$B = \{b, d, g\}$

the set of letters corresponding to voiceless stops
$$C = \{p, t, k\}$$

the set of letters in A or in B (or in both)
$$D = A \text{ or } B = \{a, b, c, d, e, g\}$$

the set of stops (letters either in B or in C)
$$E = B \text{ or } C = \{p, t, k, b, d, g\}$$

the set of letters which are in both A and B
$$F = A \text{ and } B = \{b, d\}$$

the set G of letters which are in both B and C at the same time is empty but it is still called an event. In other words B and C are mutually exclusive events, while A and B are not.

The next step is to assign positive real numbers as probabilities or weights to each outcome in such a way that the sum of all the weights is 1. The probability of an event is then taken to be the sum of the probabilities of the individual outcomes which make up the event. If all the outcomes are equally likely to occur, then it makes sense to assign the same probability to each. To do this for the example where the set S consists of 26 letters of the alphabet a weight w must be chosen so that $26\,w = 1$ or $w = \frac{1}{26}$. Then the probability of each letter is chosen to be $\frac{1}{26}$:

$$P(a) = P(b) = P(c) = \ldots = P(z) = \frac{1}{26}.$$

Once probabilities have been assigned to each outcome, probabilities can immediately be calculated for any event:

$$P(A) = P(a) + P(b) + P(c) + P(d) + P(e) = \frac{5}{26}$$

$$P(B) = \frac{3}{26}$$

$$P(C) = \frac{3}{26}$$

$$P(D) = P(A \text{ or } B) = \frac{6}{26}$$

$$P(E) = P(B \text{ or } C) = \frac{6}{26}$$

$$P(F) = P(A \text{ and } B) = \frac{2}{26}$$

$$P(G) = P(B \text{ and } C) = 0 \quad \text{fortunately}$$

$$P(S) = 1$$

Instead of assigning probabilities so that all letters are equiprobable it is perfectly possible to set:

$$P(a) = .08$$
$$P(b) = P(d) = P(g) = .02$$
$$P(c) = .03$$
$$P(e) = .10$$

say, so long as the rest are chosen so that all the probabilities together add up to 1. In this case:

$$P(A) = .08 + .02 + .03 + .02 + .10 = .25$$
$$P(B) = .06$$

If there is no other theoretical basis for assigning probabilities, then they are usually estimated by the relative frequency:

$$P(x) = \frac{m}{n}$$

where m is the number of times outcome x occurs in a sequence of n trials. As examples, if $\langle u \rangle$ occurred 277 times in a text of 10000 letters, its relative frequency, and therefore its probability would be:

$$P(u) = \frac{277}{10000} = .0277 \text{ or } 2.7\%$$

Similarly, if *sandwich* occurred 4 times in a corpus of 2000 words, its relative frequency, and therefore its probability would be:

$$P(sandwich) = \frac{4}{2000} = .002.$$

Where there is some theoretical basis for assigning probabilities to each outcome, it is to be expected that the relative frequencies will come closer and closer to the theoretical probabilities as the number of trials increases. Note that relative frequencies are by definition nonnegative real numbers, no bigger than one, since the number of occurrences of a given outcome can never be greater than the number of trials. Also the sum of the relative frequencies of all the possible outcomes is 1 and the relative frequency of an event is the sum of the relative frequencies of the outcomes which make up that event. Thus relative frequencies satisfy the requirements stated above for the assignment of probabilities.

What is the reason for setting up these requirements? Probability theory may be built up from four basic axioms and its results are available for use whenever these axioms are satisfied. These axioms are:

(1) $0 \leq P(A) \leq 1$

for any event A. If the probability is 0 the event is impossible. If the probability is 1 the event is certain.

(2) $P(S) = 1$ or $\sum_{i=1}^{k} P(x_i) = 1$,

where $x_1, x_2, \ldots, x_k$ are the elements of S. That is, the sum of all the probabilities of all the outcomes is equal to 1. If a text has only the letters $\langle a \rangle$, $\langle b \rangle$, $\langle c \rangle$ and they occur with a relative frequency of $\frac{1}{2}, \frac{1}{4}, \frac{1}{4}$ respectively, then:

$$P(\text{letter}) = P(a) + P(b) + P(c) = \frac{1}{2} + \frac{1}{4} + \frac{1}{4} = 1,$$

(3) $P(\text{not } A) = 1 - P(A)$

That is, the probability of the event not-A occurring is the complement of the probability of A. From the previous example, the probability of all letters which are not $\langle a \rangle$, say, is:

$$1 - \left(\frac{1}{4} + \frac{1}{4} \right) = \frac{1}{2}.$$

The method of assigning probabilities outlined above will ensure that axiom (3) holds, for:

$$P(A) + P(\text{not } A) = \underbrace{[P(a_1) + P(a_2) + ... + P(a_j)]}_{\text{for all the elements of } A} +$$

$$+ \underbrace{[P(a_{j+1}) + ... + P(a_k)]}_{\text{for all the elements not in } A} =$$

$$= \underbrace{P(a_1) + ... + P(a_k)}_{\text{for all the elements of } S} = 1$$

(4) $P(A \text{ or } B) = P(A) + P(B)$

where A and B are any two mutually exclusive events ($\#3$ is in fact a special case of $\#4$ and thus is not always stated separately). For example, if an adjective, a determiner, a noun, or a verb can occur in sentence initial position and their respective probabilities are known, then the probability of one of the first three occurring is:

$$P(adj \text{ or } det \text{ or } noun) = P(adj) + P(det) + P(noun)$$

This relationship will not hold when the two sets are not mutually exclusive as in sets A and B of the first example.

At times we need to investigate conditional probabilities, such as the probability that A has occurred, given that event B has already occurred. This is written $P(A|B)$ or sometimes $P_B(A)$. So long as event B is possible, i.e. $P(B) \neq 0$,

$$P(A|B) = \frac{P(A \text{ and } B)}{P(B)},$$

or in other words:

$$P(A \text{ and } B) = P(B) \cdot P(A|B).$$

Similarly,

$$P(A \text{ and } B) = P(A) \cdot P(B|A).$$

For example, in the general case of an experiment with n trials, if the event B occurs on the average m times, and in every sequence of m such trials in which the event B is observed, the result A occurs 1 time, then in every sequence of n trials, the simultaneous occurrence of the events B and A will be observed on the average 1 time. That is, if:

$$P(B) = \frac{m}{n},$$

and

$$P(A|B) = \frac{1}{m},$$

then:

$$P(A \text{ and } B) = \frac{1}{n} = \frac{m}{n} \cdot \frac{1}{m}$$
$$= P(B) \cdot P(A|B) = P(A) \cdot P(B|A).$$

To put it in somewhat different words, the probability of the simultaneous occurrence of two events equals the product of the probability of the first event with the conditional probability of the second, computed under the assumption that the first event has occurred.

If $P(A|B) = P(A)$, that is if the knowledge that event B has taken place does not affect the probability of A, then A and B are called independent events. In this case:

$$P(A \text{ and } B) = P(B) \cdot P(A|B) = P(B) \cdot P(A).$$

But then:

$$P(B) \cdot P(A) = P(A) \cdot P(B) = P(A \text{ and } B) = P(A) \cdot P(B|A)$$

and it follows that $P(B|A) = P(B)$ also.

More generally, the probability of the simultaneous occurrence of any number of mutually independent events equals the product of the probabilities of those events. As an example, in a famous study by the Russian mathematician Markov in 1913, out of 20,000 letters in a sample from Pushkin's *Eugene Onegin* there were the following consonant (*c*) and vowel (*v*) digrams and trigrams (from Miller and Chomsky 1963: 424):

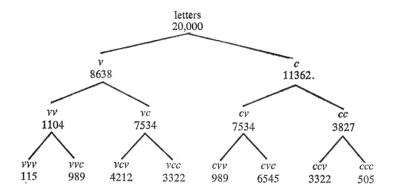

Now $P(v) = \dfrac{8638}{20000} = .432$. If the successive letters were independent, then we would expect $P(v|c)$ to equal $P(v|v)$ and both to equal $P(v)$. But from the chart we find:

$$P(v|c) = \frac{7534}{11362} = .663.$$

This is greater than .432, the probability of *v*, and greater than $P(v|v) = \dfrac{1104}{8638} = .128$. It must be that Russian vowels are more likely to occur after consonants than after vowels, that is, that they are not independent (something obvious, of course, to anyone who knows Russian).

2

STOCHASTIC PROCESSES

A stochastic process is usually defined as a probabilistic model of a physical process whose evolution is a function of time. If we represent the outcomes of the dependent trials as a random variable which is a function itself of the real variable time t, then we can say that a stochastic process is a set of time-dependent random variables. Such a model for linguistics has been proposed explicitly by Hockett and others, see for example Hockett 1955 and more particularly Hockett 1961: 220 "a grammatical system must be viewed as a stochastic process."

If the parameter space T (that is, the set of all parameter values = the domain of the function) and the state space S (that is, the set of all its states = the range of the function) are discrete,[1] the stochastic process is called a CHAIN.

The discrete linguistic units in the chain are simply concatenated. There is no distinction of any kind of linguistic levels (e.g. a P-marker). The sentences of language L are finite and are formed from the elements of an arbitrary finite set V, the vocabulary. If $\varphi, \chi \in L$ and if $\widehat{\varphi \chi}$ is the result of concatenating them in that order to form a new sequence ψ, then $\psi \in L$, that is, ψ is also a string in L. L is therefore closed under the binary operation of concatenation. Concatenation is also associative,

---

[1] Miller and Chomsky (1963, "Finitary models of language users": 273) state: "Communication systems can be thought of as discrete because of the existence of what communication engineers have sometimes called a *fidelity criterion* (Shannon, 1949). A fidelity criterion determines how the set of all signals possible during a finite time interval should be partitioned into subsets of equivalent signals – equivalent for the receiver. A communication system may transmit continuous signals precisely, but if the receiver cannot (or will not) pay attention to the fine distinctions that the system is capable of registering, the fidelity of the channel is wasted."

$$(\varphi \widehat{\ } \chi) \widehat{\ } \psi = \varphi \widehat{\ } (\chi \widehat{\ } \psi)$$

The empty sequence is the identity element, that is $cat\widehat{\ } = \widehat{\ }cat$ $= cat$ (in addition, such an identity element is 0, in multiplication it is 1). A set which includes an identity element and is closed under an associative operation is called a MONOID. A monoid satisfies three of the four postulates of a group (it has no inverse), and can therefore be called a semigroup.

We will assume that there is a finite number of experiments or states, and that there is a finite number of outcomes for each experiment. We will further assume that if all the outcomes of the experiments which precede a given experiment are known, then both the outcomes for this experiment and the probability that any particular outcome will occur are known and we want to make predictions about the process as a whole.

For example, such a process could consist of choosing letters, or vowels and consonants, or whole words, or grammatical categories where we know the possible set of letters or words or grammatical categories which can appear next in a string and the probabilities of these experiments based only on their frequency of occurrence or on the preceding symbol(s) (if the outcome depends only on the immediately preceding item, then the process is called a MARKOV CHAIN).

Let us assume that we want to simulate the process of writing graphic English sentences by choosing one letter at a time out of the possible 26 (ignoring space) and concatenating it to the previously occurring letter. Suppose also that they are independent events, that is, the probability of a letter was calculated solely on the relative frequency of each letter in a text. Finally, suppose that our sentences are only five letters long.

In the post-silence or page-initial state there are 26 possible letters with probabilities equivalent to the relative frequency of each letter, for example,[2]

$$P(e) = .131$$
$$P(t) = .090$$

[2] These frequencies are from Saires (1956, *Cryptanalysis*: 219).

$$P(o) = .082$$
$$P(a) = .078$$
$$P(n) = .073$$
$$\vdots$$

We can represent part of the generation of a five letter sentence by the following tree:

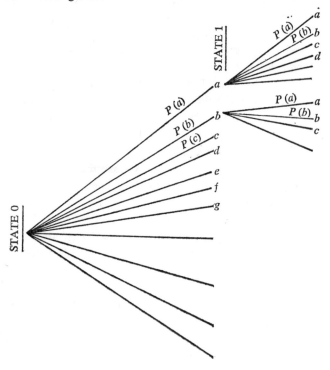

A sentence would be represented by a five step path through the tree. An example of English text generated by such a model which assumes that the choice of a letter is independent of all other letters but is chosen based on the probability (= relative frequency) of English letters (including space) is the following so-called 1st order approximation[3]:

[3] These and the other examples of approximations to English are from Shannon and Weaver (1963, *The mathematical theory of communication*).

ocro hli rgwr nmielwis eu ll nbnesebyath eei alh
enttpa oobttva nah brl

Notice that in this case all the 26 letters are possible, and also that the probabilities at each state/branch point equals 1, that is, $P(a) + P(b) + P(c) + \ldots = 1$.

If these were English words rather than letters the output would look something like:

representing and speedily is an good apt or came can.

For digrams, that is, for a letter dependent on the immediately preceeding letter (a Markov chain) we can calculate the probabilities in the following way:

$$P(t \text{ and } h) = P(th) = .0315^4$$
$$P(in) = .0169$$
$$P(er) = .0154$$

$$\cdot \qquad \cdot$$
$$\cdot \qquad \cdot$$

and

$$P(h|t) = \frac{P(t \text{ and } h)}{P(t)} = \frac{P(th)}{P(t)} = \frac{.0315}{.090} = .35.$$

When dependencies are introduced, the number of possibilities decreases, but the probabilities still equal 1.

For this Markov chain the following tree obtains:

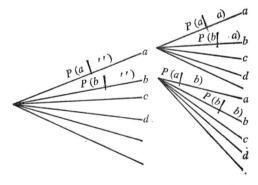

---

4   From Saires (1956, *Cryptanalysis*: 218).

An example from English (2nd order approximation)

> letters: *on ie antsoutinys are t inctore st be*
> words: *the head and in frontal attack on an.*

For trigrams, that is, for a letter dependent on the immediately preceding two letters:

$$P(th \text{ and } e)\ P(the)\ =\ .001182$$
$$P(ing)\ =\ .000356$$
$$P(and)\ =\ .000284$$

$$\therefore\ P(e|th)\ =\ \frac{P(th \text{ and } e)}{P(th)}\ =\ \frac{.001182}{.0315}\ =\ .037.$$

For trigrams a 3rd order approximation would be like:

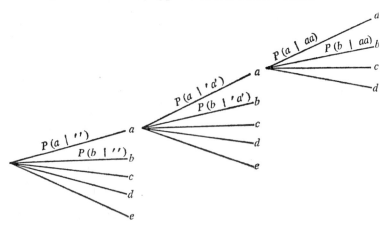

An output from such a process would be:

> letters: *in no ist lat whey cratict froure birs*
> words: *family was large dark animal came roaring down the.*

There are at least two other, related, ways of representing stochastic processes which are somewhat more compact. One is by a matrix and the other, equivalent, way is by a transition or state diagram.

A simple example can be achieved by adapting Markov's example with an additional allowance for space, as well as for consonant and vowel.

We can estimate the transitional probabilities by calculating the relative frequency of a vowel, a consonant, and a space from some sample of text. We then calculate the relative frequency of *vv, vc, cv, cc, vs, cs, sv, sc.* To find the transitional probability of going to a vowel, consonant, or space given a vowel, consonant or space we divide the relative frequency of a digram containing that item as a second member by the relative frequency of the first member. Our tree might look like the following:

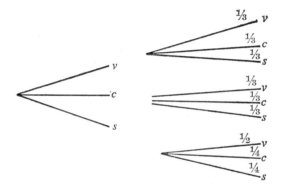

The matrix representation of this process takes the form of a table of transitional probabilities:

2nd member of digram

		P_v	P_c	P_s
1st member of digram	P_v	P_{vv}	P_{vc}	P_{vs}
	P_c	P_{cv}	P_{cc}	P_{cs}
	P_s	P_{sv}	P_{sc}	P_{ss}

For the sake of argument let us use those probabilities shown in the tree diagram. We will assume that all transitions are possible but the probabilities are different except for P_{cv} and P_{vc} which are equal (Note that since a row represents all the possible transitions from a given state, the sum of the row must equal 1).

	P_v	P_c	P_r
P_v	1/3	1/3	1/3
P_c	1/3	1/3	1/3
P_s	1/2	1/4	1/4

The initial state can be represented by a one-dimensional matrix, namely a vector.

If we circle each possible state and draw an arrow from each state to all states which can be crossed to (including looping, that is, the possibility of a sequence of two vowels etc.), the process could be represented by a directed graph like the following state or transition diagram.

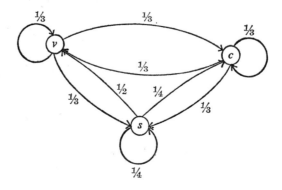

The matrix, and, therefore, the state diagram can be expanded to handle any finite number of possible states. This particular process might generate the following string:

vcvsscsvvscccvss

Being able to represent the process by a matrix allows us to use standard mathematical procedures in order to calculate various probabilities such as the probability of an ⟨ a ⟩ occurring as the fifth letter of a word; however, the linguistic interest in such a probability is rather slight.

3

INFORMATION THEORY

A particular use of a stochastic model that has found widespread use in linguistics (mainly in linguistic typology and psycholinguistics) is that suggested by the mathematical theory of communication, or as it is often called, information theory.

Information theory assumes the following model of a communication system:

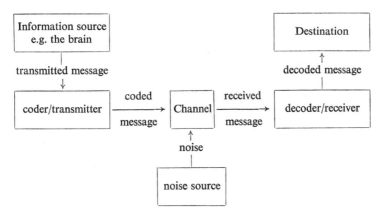

Although the model may be applied to any form of communication, it will be restricted here to language phenomena. This then restricts us to a system producing a sequence of discrete symbols chosen from a finite set of possible symbols. Further we will make the simplifying assumption that there is no noise source which will cause interference.

The information source, say, the brain, chooses a message out of a set of possible messages. This can be considered equivalent to the stochastic process that was presented in the last chapter.

The transmitter, in turn, can be conceived of as a device which will encode the message into another, common form. The reason for wanting to do this is that there are various ways of coding a message, depending on the set of symbols used. For example, one might want to consider the message as being a sequence of letters, or syllables, or graphic words. In order to handle a multiplicity of possible symbol systems and still maintain a theory general enough to handle any kind of symbol set, the encoding is performed by reinterpreting the symbols, whatever they may be, as a set of sequences of binary choices. For example, consider the system whose set of possible symbols which can be chosen in producing a message is the two geometric shapes △ and □. If the two digits 0 and 1 are adopted as the universal encoding symbol set and 0 codes △, and 1 codes □, then a message of the form:

△ □ □ △ △ □ △ □ △ △ △

would be re-coded as:

0 1 1 0 0 1 0 1 0 0 0.

If the vocabulary of geometric shapes is expanded to include ▱ and ○, four symbols would need to be encoded using 0's and 1's. This could be done unambiguously by assigning two of the digits 0 and 1 to each symbol e.g. let

△ be encoded as 00
□   01
▱   10
○   11

Then the message △ △ □ ○ ▱▱ □□□ ○ ○ would be encoded as:

00 00 01 11 10 10 01 01 01 11 11

This set can be unambiguously decoded if one knows that the encoding digits occur in pairs.

Continuing this example let the symbol set include, as well as the previous △ □ ◻ ◯ , four new shapes S X · B. Again, one would like to encode this set of symbols unambiguously by using just the digits 0 and 1. In order to do this it is necessary to use a triplet of 0's and 1's.

Let △ be encoded as 000
  □ 001
  ◻ 010
  ◯ 011
  S 100
  X 101
  · 110
  B 111

The message

· ◯ ◻B ◯ △

could be encoded as:

110 011 010 111 011 000

The encoding is just a one-to-one mapping of each symbol of the source vocabulary into a fixed-length string of 0's and 1's. A string of symbols, for instance a graphic word consisting of the letters a, s, q, r, b, p, t, y, would then be encoded by choosing the fixed-length string consisting of a sequence of 0's and 1's grouped by threes corresponding to the original sequence of letters.

As can be observed, the length of a string of 0's and 1's required to encode a set of symbols is proportional to the number of symbols in the vocabulary. When there are only two symbols, only one digit, 0 or 1 is needed; when there are four symbols, a sequence of two 0's and 1's is required; when there are eight symbols, a sequence of three 0's and 1's is needed. This observation can be captured as follows (the word BITS is usually used to mean 0 or 1, that is, a binary digit):

# of original symbols	# of bits
2	1
4	2
8	3
16	4
32	5
.	.
.	.
.	.

The relation between these two columns is that as the number of original symbols in the vocabulary is doubled, the number of bits required to code that symbol increases by one. The increase is exponential, and, in particular, the number of original symbols is proportional to a number raised to the power represented by the number of bits, namely the number 2. That is:

$$\text{\# of original symbols} = 2^{\text{\# of bits}}$$

No matter what the original symbols are or how many there are, we can always encode by a binary alphabet.

All that has been done so far is to set up the coding alphabet. What can be done with this system of channels of binary digits?

In a practical sense the designer of a communication system must take into consideration the cost of transmitting a message. Factors that are involved in calculating the cost include the length of the message and the efficiency with which it can be transmitted. The cost, length, or efficiency is in no way affected by the meaning of the message but just on such a factor as how long it takes to be transmitted.

Communication theorists searched for a very long time to devise some system by which they could quantify these concepts so that they could apply them in comparing various alternative types of communication systems as to their efficiency, etc.

The model that was proposed by Shannon was stochastic. That is, he considered a message to be generated from a known and finite set of symbols each occurring with a probability previously calculated for it from empirical observation and assigned to it as one of its properties. The process of generation can consequently be viewed as a process of choosing probabilities. If the vocabulary consists of just two symbols, then it is ARBITRARILY said that the information associated with the situation is 1. This is the standard or unit measure of information.

For example, in the case of the two possible symbol choices:

△ or □

the amount of information conveyed by this situation is 1. This situation can also be represented by a relay, the 'on' position representing △; and the 'off', □. Two of these relays can handle four symbols:

Symbol	Relay 1	Relay 2
△	off	off
□	off	on
⧄	on	off
○	on	on

For example, turning relay 1 'on' and relay 2 'off' represents ⧄. Three relays could handle eight symbols:

Symbol	Relay 1	Relay 2	Relay 3
△	off	off	off
□	off	off	on
⧄	off	on	off
○	off	on	on
S	on	off	off
X	on	off	on
·	on	on	off
B	on	on	on

(This is analogous to the 0, 1 situation above). For example, turning relay 1 'on', relay 2 'off' and relay 3 'on' represents X. Or to put it somewhat differently, three choices have to be made in order to encode a symbol.

As stated above a situation of a possible choice between two items represents one unit of information. It would be nice to be able to say that a situation represented by two relays corresponds to twice the amount of information as one relay, and one represented by three relays by thrice the amount of information. As demonstrated earlier:

$$\# \text{ of original symbols} = 2^{\# \text{ of bits}}$$

When:

$$y = m^x$$

then:

$$x = \log_m y$$

therefore:

$$\# \text{ of bits} = \log_2 (\# \text{ of original symbols}).$$

The exponential character which was observed previously for the relation of original symbols in the vocabulary to the number of bits needed to encode these symbols and the desire to express the unit of information as a sequence of choices between two symbols now allows the amount of information associated with a situation consisting of a choice from a vocabulary of n possible symbols to be defined as:

$$I = \log_2 n$$

where I is the amount of information measured in bits per symbol.
   Therefore:

n	I
2	1
4	2
8	3
16	4
32	5
.	.
.	.
.	.

which is exactly what was obtained in determining the number of bits required to code a set of symbols. Since this is the optimal code for a given set of symbols, I can be interpreted as the maximum amount of information characterizing that situation. For example, for a choice of 26 independent, equiprobable English letters $I = 4.68$.

Two conclusions can be drawn from these tables.

(1) THE AMOUNT OF INFORMATION INCREASES AS THE NUMBER OF POSSIBLE SYMBOLS INCREASES. This can be interpreted as an increase in uncertainty as the total number of possible choices increases.

(2) The probabilities of occurrence for these symbols have not yet been considered. In fact the symbols have been considered equiprobable. Therefore, THE MAXIMUM INFORMATION FOR A SITUATION IS ONE WHERE THE SYMBOLS ARE ALL EQUALLY LIKELY TO OCCUR.

For the most part, however, language data does not follow the case that any member of the set of symbols is as equally likely to occur as another. For example, the relative frequency of an English $\langle e \rangle$ is greater than that of $\langle q \rangle$. Also, English letters are not independent events, but rather dependent on the occurrence of preceding letters.

This discussion of the stochastic model of communication theory can be extended by keeping the individual symbols independent, but assigning to them the probability that they have in actual running text.

Shannon has suggested the following measure of information for such a situation:

$$H = - K \sum_{i=1}^{n} P_i \log P_i,$$

where P_i is the probability of a particular symbol and where the minus is introduced in order to get a positive answer (because a probability is a fraction and the log of a fraction is negative). If the logs are to the base 2, then K, the unit of information, is 1 and the equation can be simplified to:

$$H = - \sum_{i=1}^{n} P_i \log_2 P_i \text{ bits/symbol.}$$

In the special case where the n symbols are equiprobable, $P_i = \dfrac{1}{n}$, and:

$$H = -\sum_n \frac{1}{n} \log_2 \frac{1}{n} = -n \frac{1}{n} \log_2 \frac{1}{n}$$

$$= -\log_2 \frac{1}{n} = -(\log_2 1 - \log_2 n)$$

$$= -(0 - \log_2 n) = \log_2 n$$

showing that I is a special case of H.

H is called the entropy (or 'negentropy') of a state by analogy with the measure proposed in thermodynamics because it is a measure of uncertainty or randomness of the whole system (Note: H is not the information in A symbol but rather the average). In particular if, for a set of symbols, one of the set has a probability of 1 and the others have a probability of 0:

$$H = 1 \log_2 1 + 0 \log_2 0 \ldots$$
$$= 0$$

i.e. there is no uncertainty at all, no freedom of choice, no information.

The greatest amount of information will occur when the choices are equiprobable, i.e. when one is completely free to choose among the sets of symbols, and it will be zero when the freedom of choice does not exist.

$$H_{max} = \log_2 n.$$

The actual entropy of a source can then be compared to its maximum value and a measure of the efficiency of the coding can be obtained. This measure is called the relative entropy:

$$H_{rel} = \frac{H}{H_{max}}.$$

That is, H_{rel} measures how free the system is compared to what it actually could be if the symbols were equiprobable. A measure for the statistical constraints imposed by the system can then be given by its complement:

Redundancy $= 1 - H_{rel}$.

That is that part of the message that could be omitted and still be reconstructable; or to put it differently, if all English words consisted of five letter sequences, it would be very difficult to remember them and keep them apart. Instead words are of various lengths and combinations of letters.

The process can be extended to include the amount of information in dependent events. For a discrete source, such as a finite state grammar where for each state i there is a set of probabilities $p(j|i)$ of producing the symbol j, then there is an entropy H_i for each state. The entropy of the source will then be the average of this H_i weighted with the probability of occurrence of the states involved:

$$H = \sum_i P_i H_i$$
$$= - \sum_{i,j} P_i \, p(j|i) \log_2 p(j|i)$$

This is the entropy of the source per symbol.

One of the principle investigators in American linguistics who has concentrated much of his efforts in the application of information theory to language phenomena is Henry Kučera. The culmination of much of his research appears in *A comparative quantitative phonology of Russian, Czech and German* (1968) (in collaboration with George K. Monroe). In Chapter 5 of that work the authors describe the results of their analysis of the three languages mentioned in the title using the syllable as the linguistically relevant domain for their calculations of phoneme entropies. Since the number of syllables in a language is finite and small (there are only approximately 3,000 syllable types in Russian), they can be described by a finite-state model which the mathematical theory of communication presupposes.

In their study, syllables are considered to be independent events but the phonemes which compose the syllables show sequential constraints. Their task was to measure the overall degree of these constraints in the particular languages.

The results for their comparative study can be summarized as follows:

	Russian	Czech	German
H_s	2.7024	2.6541	2.3618
H_{rel}	0.5012	0.5134	0.4642
R	49.88%	48.66%	53.58%

From these results it is obvious that the two Slavic languages, Russian and Czech, are more efficiently structured with respect to the phonemic composition of the syllables. Also, even though their syntactic and phonological surface structures have diverged quite noticeably over the past thousand years, their syllable structures have remained relatively stable. In addition Kučera and Monroe speculate on the effect of the greater degree of inflection in the Slavic languages over German on their calculations and the interest this may have to typology.

There have been other areas in linguistics to which these probabilistic concepts have been applied. One of these areas is lexical statistics, the subject of the following chapter.

4

LEXICAL STATISTICS

The area of quantitative linguistics which has the longest history and widest applicability is probably the quantitative study of vocabulary. The reason for this is that users of natural language data such as foreign language teachers, psychologists, researchers in machine translation and computer sciences have all realized the need to know the relative frequency of word forms in their designing of efficient and controlled teaching materials, designing verbal tests, and processing natural language data. There have been word counts of wide circulation of all the major modern European languages in existence for decades and new ones appearing all the time. The reasons for creating new word counts is an outcome of a basic question in lexical statistics, namely, what is it that should be counted. The different possible answers result in the most part from different research purposes and give rise to the differences in the results of word counts of the same language. The problems usually revolve around three major language variables – time, genre and/or style, and what constitutes a word.

The problem of time arises in deciding whether to sample from a synchronic slice of language (which implies the definition of or rather clear delimitation of what constitutes a 'standard' form of the language and this definition may in fact vary from language to language). Examples of relative extremes in approaching a solution of this problem would be the Brown University Corpus of present-day edited American English (Kučera and Francis 1967) which contains samples from American English for the year 1961, and Josselson's Russian word count (1953) which included materials from early 19th as well as mid-20th century writers. Different premises and intuitions about the effect of time on a language and also the use to which the word count will be put will lead to such wide divergences.

The problem of genre and/or style also enters early into the selection of a corpus and also is intimately tied to the purpose for compiling a corpus from which a word count will be made. The variables involved here include whether the language samples should be from the spoken language or the written form of the language, whether they should include dialogue within written prose, what the mixture should be of informative and imaginative prose, and so forth. The choice of variables will affect the word count even among relatively high-frequency items.

The third major language variable which is involved in word count compilation is 'word' itself. The term 'word' in lexical statistics is usually used in one of the two following senses – either as a string of graphic characters bounded by space, or as some basic, canonical or lemmatized form, for example as it might appear in a dictionary of the language, e.g. Nominative case, singular number for a noun and the infinitive form for a verb in Russian. In the first sense the English strings CAT and CATS would be considered two different words, while in the second they are considered the same word. Since word counts are established from text (rather than dictionary), a count based on 'word' in sense one treats CATS as entirely distinct from CAT as it would be from DOG. In the second sense CAT and CATS are treated as one unit. In terms of the distribution itself the count based on words in sense two gives results very distinct from a count based on sense one words since there will be many fewer distinct words (called 'types') measured for that corpus. Zipf's counts, Yules' study and the Kučera and Francis count (cf. below) have used 'word' in sense one, – that is, anything bounded by space – but Thorndike-Lorge used 'word' in sense two.

Some of the questions which the investigator must answer before he begins his count include the following (especially for a European language):

(1) Should hyphenated words be treated as one or two?
(2) Should discontinuous morphemes such as two-part verbs in English be treated as one?
(3) Should homographs be distinguished e.g. English *bear* as a noun and a verb.
(4) Should noun adjunct constructions, such as English *fire engine* be treated as one word or two?
(5) How should portmanteau morphs be segmented?
(6) What about apostrophes?
(7) What about numbers, proper nouns, abbreviations?

These are just a few of the questions that must be answered and the specific answer will depend on the language under investigation, on the purpose of the count, and on what constitutes a word in that language.

One of the interesting characteristics of vocabulary statistics which makes it different from phoneme or form class statistics (but similar to sentence structure statistics) is the size of the vocabulary (in the sense of the set of possible items which can be chosen). One aspect of word counts which was early noted is the increase in the number of different words as the text size increases. Although the rate of increase in vocabulary size V is much slower than the increase in text size N as N increases, it never does seem to asymptote, i.e., level off at some point. This does conform to traditional linguistic notions of productive word formation however, since a speaker can increase his vocabulary under necessary extralingual contexts by creating a new (within the context of text) vocabulary item.

But this is just one of the interesting facts of vocabulary statistics. Many others come to light when one examines vocabulary usage in a text in its traditional way of representation, that is, in a frequency distribution. A frequency distribution summarizes in tabular form the frequency characteristics of the vocabulary in a text. These then can be compared with distributions from other texts, or of texts of different size, period, genre, style, etc. Let us take a simple English sentence such as:

Mary is catching a taxi but John is taking a bus.

In this sentence there are 11 running words or 'tokens', but only 9 different words or 'types', namely, *Mary, is, catching, a, taxi, but, John, taking, bus.* Of these 9 types 2 of them are used twice and the 7 others are used once (words which occur only once in a text are traditionally called *hapax legomena*). A frequency distribution groups the types by their frequency of occurrence, normally in increasing order of frequency. The frequency distribution for the sample sentence above would be:

X	f_X
1	7
2	2

where f_X is the number of types which occurred with a frequency X (The total number of tokens for the sentence is calculated by multiplying each frequency by the number of types which occur at that frequency and summing these products, i.e. the total number of tokens in a sample is $\Sigma f_X\ X$; in the case of the sentence above $(7 \times 1) + (2 \times 2) = 11$.)

In addition to the increase in vocabulary as the size of the sample increases there are other characteristics of vocabulary distributions which are visible from examining them and comparing them with others. These factors must also be accounted for by any theory of vocabulary utilization. One of these factors is that the *hapax legomena* always constitute the largest class. On the other hand a very small percentage of high frequency types accounts for a very large proportion of the text. (This has serious implications in the use of vocabulary statistics. For an enlightening discussion of this fact cf. Oettinger 1960: 228-32).

In addition when comparing texts of unequal length it can be noted that:

(a) as N increases the number of frequencies represented increases,
(b) a type with any given frequency increases,
(c) the maximum frequency represented increases,

TABLE 4.1

AMERICAN NEWSPAPER ENGLISH
(According to R. C. Eldridge)

Number of Occur- rences	Number of Words	Average Number of Phonemes	Number of Occur- rences	Number of Words	Average Number of Phonemes
1	2976	(6.656)	31	6	
2	1079	(6.151)	32	4	
3	516	(6.015)	33	6	
4	294	(6.081)	34	2	
5	212	(5.589)	35	5	
6	151	(5.768)	36	3	
7	105	(5.333)	37	2	
8	84	(5.654)	39	2	
9	86	(5.174)	40	4	
10	45	(5.377)	41	1	(3.903)
11	40	(4.825)	42	7	
12	37	(5.459)	43	1	
13	25	(5.560)	44	4	
14	28	(5.00)	45	1	
15	26	(4.807)	46	2	
16	17	(5.058)	47	5	
17	18	(4.166)	48	1	
18	10	(6.100)	49	3	
19	15	(4.733)	50	3	
20	16	(4.687)	51	1	
21	13		52	3	
22	11		54	1	
23	6		55	1	(3.333)
24	8		56	1	
25	6	(3.455)	58	2	
26	10		60	1	
27	9			1	
28	6		61–4290	71	(2.666)
29	5				
30	4				

(d) the mean frequency increases but less slow than N,

(e) the cumulative proportion of *hapax legomena* decreases.

Some of these notions, especially (a) through (d) are obvious but (e) may be better visualized by considering a hypothetical text. At text initial position $N = V$ so that $V/N = N/V = 1$ and all are *hapax legomena*. As soon as there is a repetition of a word, $N > V$, $N/V > 1$ and the cumulative proportion of *hapax legomena* decreases.

One of the first attempts to account for some of these facts was the work of George K. Zipf in *The psycho-biology of language: an introduction to dynamic philology* (1968, first published in 1935). Working with a set of word frequency distributions compiled by Eldridge for American newspaper English (1911), Zipf noted that "as the number of occurrences increases, the number of different words possessing that number of occurences decreases. Yet the significant feature in the diminution of variety which attends upon an increase in frequency of usage is the orderliness with which the one decreases as the other increases – an orderliness which includes an overwhelming majority of the total number of different words of the vocabulary used in these samplings, especially in the less frequent range." (41) See Table 4.1.[1]

The relation he observed was:

$$\text{(number of words)} \ \text{(number of occurrences)}^2 = k$$

(or $f_X X^2 = k$ in our earlier notation). For English he estimated that this relation held for 98% of the types (= his "vocabulary") and 42.4% of the tokens (= his "bulk of occurrences"). Plotted on log-log paper it describes the straight line in Figure 4.1.

He noticed the change in the slope of the line as text length increased and so, at the suggestion of a friend, substituted rank for the number of words (f_X) and ordered them in decreasing

[1] Permission from MIT press to reproduce Table 4.1 and Figure 4.1 is gratefully acknowledged.

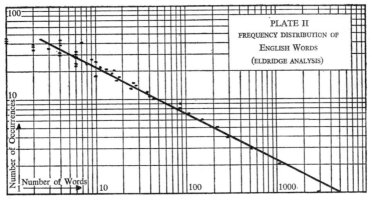

Fig. 4.1

order of frequency and consequently increasing order of rank. The distribution now looked like:

freq	rank
4290 (the word *the*)	1
2122	2
.	.
.	.

From this he drew the conclusion that for the mid-range, that is, not at the extremes,

$$f \cdot r = c$$

where c is a constant. When plotted on log-log paper, this approximates a straight line of slope -1 (except at the ends), that is, a line sloping down to the right at a 45 degree angle. This came to be known as Zipf's Law. But its status as a law or even as an interesting linguistic generality came under question in the mid-50's.

Emandations by Simon (1955) and Mandelbrot (1961) and an explanation of the Law with reference to concepts in information theory by Mandelbrot (1961), led Chomsky (1958), Halle (1958), Lees (1959), and others to criticize any and all probabilistic models of language. Their arguments are clear and very convincing.

Among their arguments against the importance of Zipf's Law is that since so many other natural phenomena unrelated to linguistics exhibit the same kind of distribution, this makes the Law completely uninteresting to linguistics. Guiraud's (1959) argument that dealing out playing cards at random and letting one of the suits stand for space will produce 'words' which follow the Zipf distribution convinces one further as to the triviality of Zipf's Law.

Another measure that has been sought by linguists (and literary critics) has been one for vocabulary richness. The one with the longest history is the ratio of types to tokens in a sample. The ratio of types to tokens in a text would seem to be a good measure of vocabulary utilization since it can specify, *inter alia*, the repetition rate of vocabulary items in a text. For example, in 100 sample texts of contemporary standard Russian compiled by the author for a study of word frequency distributions the highest type/token ratio, that is, the sample in which the greatest number of types were used among the 100 samples of almost equal size, was a group of nineteen brief news items from *Pravda* and *Izvestija* (sample A01). (See appendix I for an abbreviated description of each sample.) They were diverse in content, covering such information as the visit of Premier Longo of Italy to Moscow and the coup of the military junta in Greece in April, 1967. They may well have been written by different authors. The type/token ratio for this sample was .6668. The sample text with the lowest type/token ratio of .1774, on the other hand, was a catalogue describing various course offerings at colleges in the Soviet Union (sample H04). In this sample there is a great deal of repetition in the course offerings so that a small number of words is repeated frequently.

The type/token ratio is thus a good measure of repetitiveness or variety, but it has one serious drawback. It is very susceptible to differences in sample size: the ratio decreases rapidly as sample size increases. It can not, therefore, be used in many practical situations, such as comparing results of counts done on the works of two authors based on samples of different sizes. In this case the differences in type/token ratio could not be attributed uniquely to repetitiveness or diversity of content.

This decrease in the type/token ratio can be seen quite clearly when various representative subsets are taken from a corpus and the type/token ratio is calculated for each subset. (A 'representative' subset is a set of samples chosen from the whole corpus in such a way as to reflect the proportionate make-up of the whole corpus in terms of genre.) The only variable is the sample length, that is, the number of tokens. The results for Russian and English (the latter from Kučera 1968) are given in the following table. As before, V represents the number of types and N the number of tokens.

Russian:

Number of Samples	V	N	V/N
1	1,136	2,011	.565
10	8,954	20,342	.440
25	18,819	50,422	.373
50	30,578	100,922	.303
100	49,975	201,189	.248

English:

Number of Samples	V	N	V/N
5	2,667	10,199	.261
25	8,749	50,721	.172
50	13,725	101,557	.135
125	23,444	253,434	.093
500	50,447	1,014,225	.049

If we plot the number of types V against the number of tokens N, the growth in vocabulary with increased text length becomes clear.

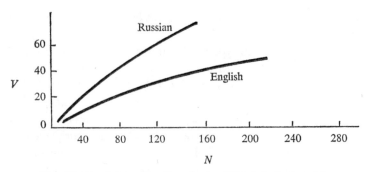

Fig. 4.2. Vocabulary *V* vs. Sample size *N* (Both in thousands).

Similarly, the decrease in the type/token ratio V/N with increased text length N can be seen if they are plotted as in Figure 4.3.

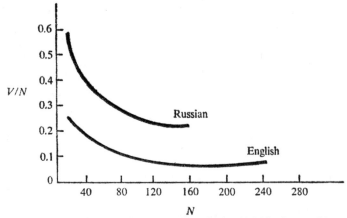

Fig. 4.3. Type/token ratio V/N vs. Sample size *N* (*N* in thousands).

In order to compensate for this variation of the ratio with respect to sample length, Herdan has suggested using the log type/log token ratio, which he calls the logarithmic type/token ratio. Herdan (1960: 26) states that "one of the most remarkable [facts] in the field of quantitative linguistics" is that "the logarithmic type/token ratio ... remains sensibly constant for samples of different size from a given literary text and is, therefore, suitable to serve as a style characteristic."

He derives this from the fact that the relation between vocabulary and text length is exponential (as is shown in Figure 4.2), and he chooses in particular to view the relation as:

$$N^t = V$$

where N is the number of tokens, that is, the length of the sample, and V is the number of types or different words in the sample. Taking the log of each side:

$$\log N^t = \log V$$
$$t \log N = \log V$$
$$t = \frac{\log V}{\log N}$$

which is the slope of the straight line resulting when $\log V$ is plotted against $\log N$.[2]

The logarithmic type/token ratio reflects the same quality of a text as the simple type/token ratio, namely the richness of vocabulary; in particular, the larger t is, the more varied or rich is the vocabulary in a sample. For example, for samples A01 and H04 the logarithmic type/token ratios are .9467 and .7725, respectively.

In actuality the logarithmic type/token ratio is also susceptible to variation due to sample length, although much more slightly than the simple type/token ratio. The accompanying table and Figures 4.4 and 4.5 illustrate this fact.

Russian:

Number of Samples	Log V	Log N	Log V/Log N
1	3.055	3.303	.924
10	3.952	4.308	.917
25	4.274	4.702	.909
50	4.485	5.003	.896
100	4.698	5.303	.886

[2] Guiraud (1959, *Problèmes et méthodes de la statistique linguistique*: 87) considers the function to be reversed, namely $N = V^a$. The advantage here is that a is then always greater than 1 and increases with sample size.

English:

Number of Samples	Log V	Log N	Log V/Log N
5	3.426	4.008	.853
25	3.941	4.705	.838
50	4.137	5.006	.826
125	4.369	5.403	.809
500	4.702	6.006	.783

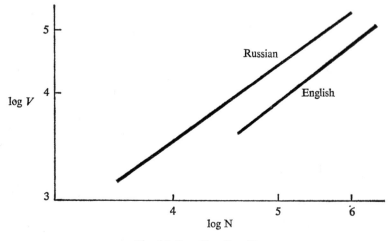

Fig. 4.4. Log V vs. Log N.

The variation in sample size (t increases inversely to the increase in sample size, that is, t decreases as N increases), is relatively slight. And as Guiraud (1959: 88) has stated, "il n'existe pas d'indice de richesse absolument indépendant de la longueur du texte."

Hence the log V/log N ratio is of the same significance in measuring vocabulary richness as V/N but it is better because it does not vary too greatly with increase in sample size. That is, it can be used profitably for samples of varying sizes as long as the variation is not too great. In either case the type/token ratio and the logarithmic type/token ratio measure only one aspect of

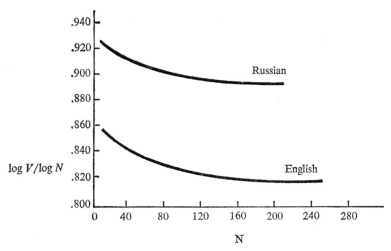

Fig. 4.5. Log V/Log N vs. Sample Size N (N in thousands).

vocabulary utilization, namely the ratio of types to tokens in a sample.

This is insufficient for a revealing lexical characterization of texts since samples with the same or similar type/token ratio may vary in other respects. For example, in sample G13, which has a type/token ratio of .6155, *hapax legomena* account for 50% of the tokens. In sample A06, which has the next lowest type/token ratio, namely .6153, the *hapax legomena* account for only 46% of the total tokens. Similarly, the most frequent word in sample G13 occurs 83 times while in A06 the most frequent word occurs only 51 times.

A more meaningful statistic would be one which would measure, and could be used to compare, the whole frequency distribution of the types, not just their total number, throughout a given sample. This would be more meaningful since the simple type/token ratio or the logarithmic type/token ratio only measures the fact that out of a given number of words used by an author a certain percentage of words was different.

One of the first attempts at accounting for these observations was by G. Udny Yule (1944). Yule in an attempt to verify the

authorship of the *De Imitatione Christi* (usually attributed to
Thomas à Kempis) compared the word distributions in that work
and in other works of à Kempis with those of works by Jean
Charles de Gerson (1363-1429) to whom attribution of the *De
Imitatione* had been made. As Yule soon noticed, even with
random sampling there always was a change in the form of the
word distribution as sample size increased. What he needed,
therefore, for his study was a "characteristic" which would be
independent of the number of occurrences. He considered the
problem to belong to a class of problems in statistics that had been
applied to the theory of personal accidents which had been
proposed to account for such facts as people who have had only
one accident are greater in number than those who have had two,
and so forth. There are differences, however, between accident
statistics and the distribution of words in texts. We do not know
the number of words 'risked' in word distributions. In accident
studies we know how many people who did not have an accident
but in word distributions we do not know how many words
were not used. For word distributions this turns out to be zero
however, since this number would be multiplied by zero, and
so the analogy is good.

As a result of his studies Yule proposed his characteristic:

$$K = 10^4 \frac{S_2 - S_1}{S_1^2}$$

where $S_1 = \Sigma f_x X$, that is, the number of tokens N in the sample
(the sample size), and $S_2 = \Sigma f_x X^2$. The factor 10^4 is used to
avoid small decimals.

As the sample size increases, S_1 increases at a much lower rate
than S_1^2 or S_2 and so Yule's characteristic may be re-interpreted
as:

$$K^* = \frac{S_2}{S_1^2} = \frac{\Sigma f_x X^2}{(\Sigma f_x X)^2}$$

As Kučera and others have shown, the ratio $X/\Sigma f_x X$ is the
estimate of the probability of words of frequency X. Substituting P

for this ratio, Yule's equation reduces to:

$$K^* = \sum_{i=1}^{m} f_x P_i^2$$

Summing for each X, we have:

$$K^* = \sum_{i=1}^{n} P_i^2$$

where n is the total number of types. This equation can be interpreted as the average repeat rate of the vocabulary in the sample, that is, a measure of the probability that two random samplings will yield the same word.

Kučera has also demonstrated that Yule's K is not a good measure of the distribution of types because the same K can be obtained for quite dissimilar distributions. The reason for this is that K does not involve explicitly the number of types and so if the number of types in two samples is different, the same K may result for very different distributions.

Because of its inability to uniquely characterize the distribution, and its failure to use the type/token ratio, Yule's K is considered to be of limited use in the measure of the lexical properties of texts.

Kučera has suggested a different approach toward such a quantitative lexical measure, one which will account for both the frequency distribution and the type/token ratio. His formulation of this measure centers around the information theoretical concept of average entropy. In particular, his measure relies on the two basic concepts of information theory discussed in chapter 3. The first is that the entropy of a system increases as the number of distinct symbols increases. Secondly, the entropy increases as the frequencies of the symbols tend toward equiprobability (at which point maximum average entropy per symbol is reached).

By modifying the formula for the measure of average entropy, Kučera characterizes the distribution of types in a sample as:

$$D = - \sum_{i=1}^{V} P_i \log P_i$$

where P_i is the proportional frequency of type i in the sample, or, in other words, the estimated probability (on the basis of that particular sample). If the absolute frequency of i is F_i, then $P_i = F_i/N$.

D is essentially a measure of the deviation of the actual distribution from the optimal equiprobable distribution. The optimal distribution will obtain when all of the types occur with the same frequency, namely $1/V$. Using this as our estimate of the probability of each type we have:

$$D = - \sum_{i=1}^{V} \frac{1}{V} \log \frac{1}{V}$$

$$= - V \left(\frac{1}{V} \log \frac{1}{V} \right)$$

$$= - \log \frac{1}{V}$$

$$= \log V.$$

In the usual case, of course, the distribution of types is not equiprobable in natural language samples. D can be re-interpreted for the non-equiprobable case by using the parameters available to us from the more usual frequency distribution, namely X, the frequency of a type, and f_x, the number of types occurring with that frequency. The formula for the distribution can be re-stated as follows:

$$D = - \sum_{x} f_x \frac{X}{N} \log \frac{X}{N},$$

where the sum is taken over all values of X, from the *hapax legomena* to the highest occurrence frequency in the sample. Since N is the sample size and since V increases as N does, D must also be dependent on sample size; it also increases as N does.

Since the resultant calculation of this D is a measure of the actual distribution of the vocabulary in a sample, and since $\log V$ represents the optimal distribution for such a sample, Kučera suggests the ratio of D to $\log V$ as an index of the relative efficiency of the vocabulary distribution in a sample, namely:

$$E = \frac{D}{\log V},$$

$$E = \frac{- \sum_{x} f_x \frac{X}{N} \log \frac{X}{N}}{\log V}.$$

The efficiency index E does not, however, include the type/token ratio, the other parameter which is felt to be needed in any overall measure of lexical utilization in addition to the frequency distribution. The same E therefore can result from two distributions with different numbers of types. For example, for a sample with an equiprobable distribution E reduces to one regardless of the number of types.

E, however, is of value since it measures the degree of deviation of an actual distribution from the optimal equiprobable distribution of a sample with the same number of types. It makes up for the deficiency observed in K, namely, the same values of E can not be obtained for two distributions of dissimilar pattern, such as an optimal and a non-optimal distribution.

In order to include some measure of the type/token ratio in any overall measure of lexical utilization Kučera proposes to calculate the ratio of the actual distribution D to $\log N$. Using the same reasoning as before, we conclude that $\log N$ is the optimum value of D which obtains only if every word in a sample is different, that is, $V = N$, so that $X = 1$ and $f_x = N = V$. Hence, Kučera proposes the following measure of lexical utilization:

$$L = \frac{D}{\log N},$$

$$L = \frac{- \sum_{x} f_x \frac{X}{N} \log \frac{X}{N}}{\log N}.$$

The calculation of values of L was made by the author for each of 100 samples from the Russian corpus mentioned earlier. The following results for L were obtained for the highest ten values (cf. Appendix II for all of the values):

A01	Press reportage: Spot news	.8888
F02	Magazine articles	.8851
A06	Press reportage: Sports	.8828
A05	Press reportage: Sports	.8793
J05	Book on Soviet music	.8789
K05	Novel	.8778
A09	Press reportage: Spot news	.8773
B06	Institutional editorials	.8765
C01	Visual Art Reviews	.8755
K12	Novel	.8751

Of these ten Russian samples with a high L seven of the samples consist of multi-item samples and four of these are from genre A (Press reportage) alone. An examination of Appendix III will help point up other correlations. In this appendix values of L for the samples of each genre are ranked in decreasing order. All of the values of L for genre A occur in the first half of the ranking except for sample A07. This sample (A07) consists of three items, one of which is longer than the other two combined. The multi-item samples are A01-A09 (all of the A genre), B01, B03-B06 (all of the B genre but one), C01, E01-E05 (also all the E genre but one), F01-F03, and R01. Of these 24 multi-item samples 22 occur in the top half of the ranking of genres by decreasing value of L. The other two, E05 which is fifty-fifth and A07 which is sixty-fourth, consist of more than one selection, but one of these is much longer than the others combined.

Similar results for English have led Kučera to interpret L as a measure of TEXTUAL CONNECTIVITY. In particular, samples consisting of several selections from various sources have a high value of L. Samples from a continuous text, however, tend to have a lower value of L.

Another lexical feature can also be associated with a low value of L. The ten samples with the lowest values of L in the Russian corpus are:

| D03 | Book on religious feast days | .8285 |
| K03 | Short story | .8272 |

N01	Adventure novel	.8171
G15	Speech on agricultural production	.8081
H05	Agricultural manual	.7929
B02	Editorial from *Izvestija*	.7675
H02	Agricultural manual	.7666
H03	Text of a treaty	.7619
H01	Laws establishing courts	.7413
H04	College catalogue	.6385

All five of the samples from genre H (Government documents, house organs and so forth) are present. H01 is a set of regulations pertaining to courts of law; H02 is a manual on certain aspects of collective farming; H03 is a treaty between the Soviet Union and Yugoslavia; H04 is the catalogue listing course offerings at various Soviet universities; and H05 deals with collective farming. B02, the fifth lowest, is an editorial from the newspaper *Izvestija*. G15 is a speech concerning agricultural production. N01 is an adventure novel by Babaevskij; K03 is a short story by Antonov, and D03 is a description of the feast days in the Russian Orthodox Church.

All of these samples consist of one selection only. This corroborates Kučera's observation that L is a relative indicator of TEXTUAL CONNECTIVITY. But in addition eight of these ten samples having the lowest values of L (all but N01 and K03 at least) also deal with very narrowly defined subjects – course offerings, regulations concerning the courts, a treaty, three texts on collective farming, and a description of church holidays. This relation between a low value of L and small variety of discourse has led Kučera to associate a low value of L with what he has termed SEMANTIC HOMOGENEITY.

The clustering of values for the individual genres can be seen graphically from Appendix III. Values of L for genre A, as we stated, are mainly in the upper half; all of the H values cluster near the bottom of the chart. Similarly, most of the values for genre B occur in the top half, while values for genre J occur in the lower half. For genre G the values of L are concentrated in the middle third. Values for genre E and F are mainly in the upper half. For P, five out of the eight samples occur in the upper half. Values for K (General fiction) are spread rather evenly as are those for D. The values for N are mainly in the lower half. Since genres C, L and R each consisted of one sample only, the significance of their relative positioning is questionable.

A more precise corroboration of these relative rankings of the genres for values of L can be indicated by ranking the mean L for each genre in a decreasing order:

Genre	Number of Samples	Mean L
C Visual Art Reviews	1	.8755
A Press: Reportage	9	.8712
L Children's Literature	1	.8634
E Skills and hobbies	6	.8602
F Popular lore	7	.8584
R Humor	1	.8556
P Historical novels	8	.8555
K General fiction	14	.8523
G Belles lettres, biographies, memoirs, speeches	16	.8499
B Press: Editorials	6	.8493
D Religion	5	.8460
N Adventure novels	6	.8441
J Learned	15	.8416
H Miscellaneous	5	.7403

An inspection of this table tends to verify the relation of a low value of L and a high degree of semantic homogeneity. All of the samples of genre H deal with specialized topics. Similarly, sample J05, which is the only one of the fifteen in its genre to be in the ten highest, is also the only sample of its genre in the top half of the ranking by sample. The relative position of B in the lower half of the list and the similarity of its absolute value with that of G (Belles lettres, etc.) lends to an interesting interpretation. Since the B samples are mostly multi-item samples, one would expect them to occupy a higher relative position in the list. However, the selections in the multi-item samples of B usually consist of one large selection and only one or two shorter items. We are therefore dealing with rather long continuous texts, which would tend to lower the value of L. Also, the similarity of the L value of B and that of G hints at the interpretation of samples from B as dealing with fairly specialized topics similar to those found in speeches or belles lettres. Editorials generally deal with a single, well-defined, specific topic and tend to have a high repeat rate of key-words. Hence, a low relative value of L for the genre B is rather easily explicable.

There are various factors of the frequency distribution which affect the value of L. An examination of some of the features of the distributions gives clues as to the possible effect of these factors on L. An investigation of the distributions of all 100 samples shows that six of the samples with the ten highest values of L also have six of the ten highest values in the number of *hapax legomena* in the corpus.

If the ten highest values of L are ranked in descending order and so are the samples of this set which also rank in the highest ten samples in terms of *hapax legomena*, also in decreasing order, we have:

Rank	L	Hapax legomena
1	A01	F02 (1136)
2	F02	A05 (1106)
3		A01 (1101)
4	A05	A09 (1083)
6		K12 (1065)
7	A09	C01 (1064)
9	C01	
10	K12	

Similarly, for the lowest ten values, in descending order, we have:

Rank	L	Hapax legomena
93		G15 (706)
94	G15	
95	H05	H05 (590)
96	B02	B02 (505)
97	H02	H03 (480)
98	H03	H02 (398)
99	H01	H01 (364)
100	H04	H04 (143)

In this case seven samples appear on both lists for each parameter. There seems, therefore to be a distinct correlation between a high value of L and a high number of *hapax legomena* in a sample. The effect of difference in sample size, however, tends to diminish the reliability of the correlation somewhat for the higher values. When the PERCENTAGES of tokens in a sample which are accounted for by *hapax legomena* are also ranked in decreasing order, we find only four samples appearing on both lists instead of six:

Rank	L	Percentage of tokens accounted for by *hapax legomena*
1	A01	F02 (56.01 %)
2	F02	A01 (54.34 %)
3		K12 (53.70 %)
5		C01 (52.88 %)
9	C01	
10	K12	

Since a percentage nullifies the differences in sample size, this indication of correlation is more accurate. At the other end of the scale, that is, for the low values of L, the correlation between a low value of L and a relatively small percentage of *hapax legomena* is even better:

Rank	L	Percentage of tokens accounted for by *hapax legomena*
94	G15 ———————————— G15 (33.73 %)	
95	H05 ———————————— H05 (29.79 %)	
96	B02 ———————————— B02 (25.36 %)	
97	H02 ⟍ ⟋ H03 (23.57 %)	
98	H03 ⟋ ⟍ H02 (19.82 %)	
99	H01 ———————————— H01 (18.00 %)	
100	.H04 ———————————— H04 (7.14 %)	

The correlation of L with the percentage of TYPES accounted for by *hapax legomena*, especially for high values of L, is very poor – only one of the ten samples with high L also has a high percentage of types accounted for by *hapax legomena*. This is sample F02. This is not too unexpected since L is defined as a relation between the frequency distribution and the optimal distribution of a sample of the same length; in other words the calculation of L takes the number of tokens into consideration directly, but does not explicitly involve the types. For samples of similar size, we can conclude that there is a correlation between the number of *hapax legomena* in a sample and the value of L, and the relation is direct. A large number of *hapax legomena* in a sample implies a high value of L.

Another parameter that may affect the value of L is the actual frequency with which the most frequent type occurred. A thorough investigation of the whole corpus points toward a correlation, an inverse one, however, between L and the frequency of the most frequent type in each sample. If we rank the samples with the highest ten values of L again in decreasing order and match them against the samples ranked according to the type with the highest frequency in that sample in ASCENDING order we have:

Rank	L	Frequency of type with highest frequency	Rank
3	A06 ———————— A06 (51)		1
6	K05 ⟍ ⟋ K12 (59)		5
10	K12 ⟋ ⟍ K05 (64)		8

This inverse relation is even more apparent at the other end of the scale:

Rank	L	Frequency of type with highest frequency	Rank
93	N01	G15 (113)	93
94	G15	H05 (117)	94
95	H05		
96	B02		
97	H02	B02 (158)	97
		H02 (166)	98
		N01 (169)	99
100	H04	H04 (251)	100

There therefore seems to be an inverse correlation between a high value of L and a low frequency for the most frequent type in the sample. Obviously, this correlation is not perfect; but it is an indication of what the index L is sensitive to.

A somewhat more extensive study was made of the effect of the high frequency types on L. The range of the high frequency portion of the distribution was increased to include the percentage of tokens accounted for by the TEN most frequent types in each sample. The inverse correlation between L and a high percentage of tokens accounted for by the ten most frequent types is much better than for the single most frequent type. This can be seen from the following two series:

Ten highest L's in descending order	Percentage of tokens accounted for by the ten most frequent types in ascending order
A01	A06 (12.02 %)
F02	B03 (13.46 %)
A06	A05 (13.66 %)
A05	A01 (13.67 %)
J05	K05 (13.72 %)
K05	J14 (13.89 %)
A09	E01 (13.91 %)
B06	A03 (13.99 %)
C01	F02 (14.10 %)
K12	B06 (14.10 %)

And at the other end of the scale:

Ten lowest L's in descending order	Percentage of tokens accounted for by the ten most frequent types in ascending order
D03	G15 (19.35 %)
K03	K03 (19.59 %)
N01	F06 (19.99 %)
G15	H05 (20.35 %)
H05	H02 (20.66 %)
B02	K07 (20.88 %)
H02	H01 (22.40 %)
H03	B02 (23.30 %)
H01	H03 (23.57 %)
H04	H04 (33.98 %)

It has been known that the most frequent words in a language are also those that have a very high functional load for signaling grammatical structure. They can also be considered generally to have little semantic content, their chief function being to operate in relating syntactic structures. It could thus be suspected that the frequency of these function words would play a large part in the evaluation of L. To test this hypothesis that the number of function word tokens in a sample can be correlated with values of L, sixty function words were chosen and their individual frequencies were recorded for each sample. Since most frequent words contribute rather heavily to a low value of L, it seemed pointless to pick automatically the highest frequency words many of which are function words. The function words were chosen by going through each sample and recording those types which it was felt would be generally agreed to be function words. There was no attempt to construct a list *a priori* based on the most frequent types occurring in the corpus. The circularity of defining function words as the most frequent types in a sample and then seeing whether function words affected the values of L (knowing the positive effect of the most frequent types on L) was thereby avoided.

There should be no argument with the presence of any items in the list. There may be disagreement on what was omitted, however. The negative particle *ne* with a very high expected frequency was omitted, as were pronouns. In either case some might not agree on their exclusion. The list actually chosen consists for the most part of prepositions, conjunctions, and particles – from the most frequent type *i* to one of the least frequent *jakoby*. The complete list appears in Appendix IV.

The percentage of function words with respect to the total tokens was calculated for each sample. As was the case with the ten most frequent types, the relation was inverse. Owing to the contribution of low frequency function words in the total, however, the relation is not close at all.

Ten highest values of L in descending order	Function word tokens as percentage of total tokens in ascending order.
A01	H04 (13.34 %)
F02	A06 (14.46 %)
A06	J05 (15.28 %)
A05	A01 (15.64 %)
J05	G01 (16.12 %)
K05	J12 (16.20 %)
A09	E01 (16.42 %)
B06	D01 (16.55 %)
C01	A02 (16.58 %)
K12	J14 (16.68 %)

The most obvious surprise in terms of the rest of this list is to find H04 at the top, that is, the sample with the lowest value of L is ranked right along with those samples with the highest values of L. This can be accounted for by the fact that there are only six function words in the whole sample. Also, one of these six types, *i*, accounts for 94 % of the function word tokens. Sample H04 is very unusual in many ways, as has been pointed out. It has only one function word among the ten most frequent types in the sample, eight of the others being nouns and one an adjective. Six of the ten most frequent types which occur in the corpus do not occur in H04. These are *ne, s, čto, a, k, kak.* (Nine of the ten most frequent words in the corpus are among the function words studied. The only one absent is *ne,* the fourth most frequent.) The effect of function words on L is obviously minor; inversely, the effectiveness of L as a relative measure of the frequency of function words in a sample is poor. But again if there is any correlation, it is an inverse one. This becomes clearer when observing the other end of the scale:

Ten lowest values of L in descending order	Function word tokens as percentage of total tokens in ascending order
D03	F05 (20.95 %)
K03	K11 (20.96 %)
N01	D03 (21.16 %)
G15	G09 (21.21 %)
H05	R01 (21.25 %)
B02	N02 (21.35 %)
H02	G12 (21.45 %)
H03	K07 (21.83 %)
H01	P05 (22.69 %)
H04	N01 (23.14 %)

Only two samples are in both columns. Also, none of the samples from genre H is represented. It seems, therefore, that the percentage of tokens accounted for by the function words in a sample has very slight effect on the value of L, at least for the function words used in this study. These included both high frequency and low frequency types. If we chose a less broad frequency range of function word types and, in effect, equated a set of function words with high frequency words, the obvious result would be a closer inverse correlation.

As this discussion indicates, L seems to be affected by at least two major factors of the word frequency distribution. A very high value of L would probably be characterized by a large number of *hapax legomena* and a relatively small number of high frequency tokens. That is, L is a measure of the reliance of a sample on the rarer words in a sample. This is most probably due to the fact that L includes the logarithmic type/token ratio, which is high for a sample with a large number of different types (for the most part, *hapax legomena*). Also, although function word types account for a relatively large number of the sample tokens, their effect is much less pronounced than the more clear relation between a low value of L and a high number of high frequency types (or percentage of tokens accounted for by high frequency types).

Because the Kučera index L can accurately characterize many features of the frequency distribution of lexical items and can be interpreted in an interesting and meaningful way, it can be a valuable aid in comparing the lexical utilization of words within the texts of the same genre, that is, as a measure of lexical style, an aspect of individual performance quite important in literary criticism.

Twenty-five of the 100 samples of approximately 2,000 running words used in building the corpus described in this chapter are from novels. These novels were chosen at random, as were the specific passages. The only stipulations were that quoted material account for no more than fifty percent of the passage, and that the authors be, as well as could be determined, native speakers of Russian. The samples represent, intuitively at least, a broad range of styles and are representative of novels published in the Soviet Union in that period.

The values of L in descending order for these novels are listed in Table 4.2.

(The mean for these samples is .8536; the median, .8519; and the standard deviation, .0154. Only one novel, the last one in Table 4.2, Babaevsky's *Native Land* falls beyond two standard deviations from the mean.)

The results of the calculation of L for each sample and the interpretation of L as a measure of semantic homogeneity allow us to draw some interesting conclusions about the lexical style of these novels. First, the simplifying assumption must be made that a 2,000 running word sample of text can be considered

TABLE 4.2

Novels by decreasing value of L

Author and Title	L
Antonovič A. *People thirst for truth* (Ljudi žaždut pravdy)	.8779
Tendrjakov, V. *Rendez-vous with Nefertiti* (Svidanie s Nefertiti)	.8751
Lebedinskij, Ju. *Fire-glow* (Zarevo)	.8743
Koževnikov, V. *Shield and sword* (Ščit i meč)	.8729
Kazakov, N. *When anger inflames hearts* (Kogda gnev obžigaet serdca)	.8718
D'jakov, B. *A story of past experience* (Povest' o perežitom)	.8703
Vitra, N. *Swiftly-passing days* (Bystro-beguščie dni)	.8669
Kočetov, V. *The secretary of the oblast' committee* (Secretar' obkoma)	.8660
Sokolov, A. *Menšikov*	.8625
Solouxin, V. *Mother-mother-in-law* (Mat' -mačexa)	.8568
Bondarev, Ju. *Quiet* (Tišina)	.8550
Simonov, K. *Comrads in arms* (Tovarišči po oružiju)	.8541
Zlobin, S. *Island bully* (Ostrov bujan)	.8519
Zadornov, N. *Father Cupid* (Amur-batjuška)	.8509
Sartakov, S. *An icy treasure* (Ledjanoj klad)	.8500
Paustovskij, K. *Smoke of the fatherland* (Dym otečestva)	.8494
Šaginjan, M. *The first all-Russian* (Pervaja vserossijskaja)	.8471
Ketlinskaja, V. *To live otherwise is worthless* (Inače žit' ne stoit)	.8450
Kazakov, Ju. *Light blue and green* (Goluboe i zelenoe)	.8415
Solženicyn, A. *One day in the life of Ivan Denisovič* (Odin den' Ivana Denisoviča)	.8399
Bregova, D. *The path of discoveries* (Doroga iskanij)	.8373
Trifonov, Ju. *The drowning of thirst* (Utoplenie žaždy)	.8368
Lidin, V. *The heart of one's shadow* (Serdce svoego ten')	.8365
Dudincev, V. *A New Year's tale* (Novogodnaja skazka)	.8330
Babaevskyj, S. *Native land* (Rodimyj kraj)	.8171

representative of the lexical make-up of the whole work.[3] Then one can firmly state, for example, that the lexical character of Tendrjakov's *Rendezvous with Nefertiti* ($L = .8751$) or Libedinskij's *Fire-glow* ($L = .8743$) is characterized by much greater semantic heterogeneity than Jurij Kazakov's *Light blue and green* ($L = .8415$), Solženicyn's *One day in the life of Ivan Denisovič* ($L = .8399$), or Dudincev's *A New Year's tale* ($L = .8330$).

[3] For an interesting discussion of the opposite assumption, that is, that in exceptional cases samples from different parts of a text may differ substantially, see Doležel (1967, "The Prague School and the statistical theory of poetic language": 102).

The individual style of a literary work is usually characterized by a whole series of parameters in addition to the frequency distribution of lexical items. Traditionally lexical utilization has been and will continue to be one of the features used in comparing individual styles. However, what is probably of more interest to the literary critic (than, perhaps, the style analyst) is how this stylistic feature is operating within the work as a whole, that is, how it is functioning in a particular novel. A meaningful analysis of the stylistic devices used in a literary work can only be achieved with correlations between the stylistic devices and the possible semantic (in a broad sense) interpretations of the work.

As an example, from the standpoint of comparative stylistics the analysis of the semantic homogeneity in Solženicyn and the heterogeneity in Tendrjakov may lead to a criticism incorrectly valuing Tendrjakov, if the sole criterion used for the criticism is semantic homogeneity. It is in fact probably just the opposite – the low value of L in Solženicyn may be the stylistic device which is operating most crucially in the whole work. This novel is about prison life and so the oppressive feeling of the daily routine may be being achieved by a high repeat rate in the vocabulary. Also, since the main character is uneducated and has difficulty in understanding the conversation of the intellectuals in the camp, Solženicyn may have used semantic homogeneity as the principal device in capturing this characterization. The decision on how semantic homogeneity is functionally operating within a work, depends, then, on its correlation with other features. But the Kučera index L is a valuable tool in determining semantic homogeneity in a text and it can, therefore, serve as a useful measure of lexical style – one performance characteristic with a long tradition and established interest.

5

A PROBABILISTIC PERFORMANCE MODEL

The survey of probabilistic models presented in the preceding four chapters concentrated on the development of finite-state models, especially as they underlie the linguistic applications of the mathematical theory of communication. The reason for this emphasis is that a great deal of research has been conducted in this area. The first doubts of the validity of such models came about after Chomsky (1956) formalized the various models which had been proposed for linguistics; however, the first rather exhaustive critique of probabilistic models in language description did not appear until Miller and Chomsky (1963). In the latter work Miller and Chomsky give very convincing arguments against probabilistic models of language. Perhaps their most convincing argument is drawn from data from language acquisition.

In a relatively common sentence such as *The man who used to live down the street from us for about five years shot himself yesterday afternoon* there is a dependency between the second word *man* and the seventeenth word, the reflexive pronoun *himself*. If we assume a limited vocabulary of only 1,000 words, for an information theoretical model as described earlier we would have to estimate 10^{45} ($= 1,000^{15}$) parameters – quite a task even for a computer. If we make an even further simplifying assumption, namely that the process involves not a choice of words but rather a choice of grammatical categories and if we limit the categories to, say, noun, verb, adjective, and adverb, the parameters to be estimated are still 10^9 ($= 4^{15}$). This is a substantial reduction but if this were a model proposed as a language acquisition device, it would mean that the child would have to learn these 10^9 parameters within his childhood which lasts only 10^8 seconds!

This argument and others by Miller and Chomsky against stochastic models of language are very convincing, both from a statistical as well as a linguistic theoretical point of view. The obvious question to be raised then is: What use at all are probabilistic models in linguistics? The answer to this question has to be related to (and therefore indirectly answered by) the following two questions: What types of linguistic data can not be accounted for by a non-probabilistic model? Are there more powerful probabilistic models than those based on finite-state grammars?

Although the answer to the first question has to be tentative, relying on further inputs from psychology, neurology, sociology, etc., there is data that has not been accounted for by non-probabilistic models and which do not seem amenable to them – these are various data from language performance. In addition there have been probabilistic models proposed which are more powerful than finite-state grammars (cf. below).

The Chomskyan dichotomy of competence and performance has been challenged by some linguists (e.g., Halliday 1970, Whitaker 1971); however, it seems obvious that what a person knows and what he does are related but different phenomena and linguistics should account for the linguistic aspects of these phenomena (*pace* Lightner in Labov 1971).

There have been specific linguistic phenomena claimed as performance factors in the literature. They can be divided into two major categories, one may be called neuro-psychological and the other linguistic. The interesting neuro-psychological factors include:

(1) memory limitations, intonational and stylistic factors, 'iconic' elements of discourse (for example, a tendency to place logical subject and object early rather than late ...) (Chomsky 1965: 11);

(2) producing a sentence or 'perceiving' its structure and understanding it (Chomsky 1963: 390);

(3) rules of stylistic reordering (Chomsky 1965: 127);

(4) perceptual complexity, ease of recall (Fodor and Garrett 1966: 141);

(5) memory restrictions, inattention, distraction, non-linguistic know-
ledge and beliefs, and so on (Chomsky and Halle 1968: 3).

What might be called purely linguistic factors include:

(1) (i)   repeated nesting contributes to unacceptability,
    (ii) self-embedding contributes still more radically to unaccept-
          ability,
    (iii) multiple-branching constructions are optimal in acceptability,
    (iv) nesting of a long and complex element reduces acceptability
          (Chomsky 1965: 13);
(2) difficulty of producing right-branching structures (Chomsky and
    Halle 1968: 372);
(3) automatic disambiguation of potential ambiguities (Weinreich 1966:
    398);
(4) sequences of sounds people actually utter as opposed to those that
    an ideal speaker of the language might be supposed to utter
    (Kay 1970: 2);
(5) slips of the tongue, the sets of sentences that people find difficult to
    understand, and segments of text which embrace more than a single
    sentence (Kay 1970: 3).

At least five non-probabilistic formal performance models have
been proposed in the linguistic literature to account for some of
these factors. These are Miller and Chomsky 1963, Halle and
Stevens 1964, Wales and Marshall 1966, Schwarcz 1967, and
Fromkin 1971.

Miller and Chomsky (1963, especially 483-88) outline a model of
complicated behavior using a concept called 'tote' (test-operate-
text-exit) units which try to account for factors involved in
language learning and which operate on structures analoguous to
P-markers (this concept has recently been incorporated into a
theory by Leont'ev 1969). The test is used to see if some situation
matches an internally generated criterion; the operation then
reduces any differences between the external situation and the
internal criterion. The operation can then revise the criterion
based on new inputs or change the environment. The application
of the concept of a tote unit, however, is not developed at all in
applications to language in that article.

One of the first explicit models for performance was that for speech recognition proposed by Halle and Stevens 1964. Using an analysis by synthesis scheme, they propose a model for inputting continuous speech and outputting some sort of phonemic transcriptions. The scheme suffers however from the notorious weakness of all analysis by synthesis schemes in that they are inefficient and can not operate in real-time. (This criticism has also been raised by Fodor and Garrett 1966.)

Among the other three models mentioned above (actually Wales and Marshall call theirs a schema) the only apparent common feature is that generation is initiated with a conceptual structure as a given. The utterance generators of both Wales and Marshall and Schwarcz are quite sketchy, however. Of the three Fromkin's is the only really detailed one and the best motivated. It is a linear, one-way utterance generator. What is significant and so intriguing about the model is its justification of the ordering of various performance operations based on evidence from spoonerisms and slips of the tongue.

In no case, however, is there an attempt to represent what goes on in the various black boxes. That is, none actually relate the rules of the complete grammar with their performance compartments, not even those espousing a correlative view of competence and performance, that is, a view which considers the two members of the dichotomy as quite close.

The performance data described above should be describable by a probabilistic model but one which is more powerful than a finite-state grammar. Three such probabilistic grammatical models which have been proposed in the literature, can be applied to account for some of these linguistic phenomena. These are Greenander 1967, where a probabilistic grammar is developed for a picture processing scheme, Suppes 1970,[1] proposed to account for certain descriptive problems in child language (as well as for defining criteria for choosing grammars), and Salomaa 1969 where a formal model of a probabilistic grammar is presented.

---

[1] Hass' discussion (1970 "Properties of information – theory measure of grammatical goodness-of-fit") is framed more explicitly within information theoretical assumptions and concepts.

Greenander proposes to overcome the shortcomings of Markov models by accounting for the dependencies mentioned by Miller and Chomsky syntactically. He states this as "Hypothesis: Most of the stochastic dependence is caused by the form of the syntax." (1967: 7). He introduces this by examining the trees (usually surface) rather than the sentences generated and then imposing a probability distribution on the syntactic rules.

Following Greenander let G be a *CF* grammar with terminal vocabulary Γ_t and a set of syntactic variables Γ_v. The finite set of productions or re-write rules Π is enumerated by a natural number r ranging from 1 to p. The finite set of productions re-writing a given variable ξ is denoted by Π_ξ, so that:

$$\Pi = \bigcup_{\xi \in \Gamma_v} \Pi_\xi$$

that is, Π is the set of production rules ranging over the set of rules which expand all the various non-terminal symbols. For a given sentence $x \in \Gamma^*$ (where Γ^* is the set of terminal sentences) let T_x be the set of generation trees leading from the initial symbol σ to x. For a given generation tree T denote by $\Pi(T)$ the set of productions used at the nodes of T, taking into account the number of times a particular production has been applied.

He then defines the following. For each $\xi \in \Gamma_v$ introduce a probability distribution over Π, such that $P_r \geqq 0$, where $r \in \Pi_\xi$. In particular assign a probability to each production rule such that:

$$\sum_{r \in \Pi_\xi} P_r = 1,$$

that is, the sum of the probabilities assigned to the various rules expanding ξ must equal 1. To a generation tree T associate the probability:

$$P(T) = \prod_{r \in \Pi(T)} P_r$$

where the factor P_r appears the same number of times as the index r occurs in the set $\Pi(T)$ that is, the probability associated with a given tree is the product of the probabilities (because the rules are independent) associated with each rule used in its generation.

Greenander's full model defines a probability distribution for the set of *P*-markers generated by a *PS* grammar and an induced distribution for the set of sentences. Syntactic analysis and synthesis can then be examined from the point of view of maximum probability (and, therefore, efficiency) of correct analysis and synthesis.

In a similar vein Suppes 1970 proposes at least two factors which linguistic theory must account for. These are how one chooses the best grammar (this is obviously related to his research interests in child language) and the length and complexity of utterances ("the distribution of these features is of importance in understanding the character of actual language use" [p. 97]). A pragmatic objective of the study of probabilistic grammars is "to account for a high percentage of a corpus with a relatively simple grammar and to isolate the deviant cases that need additional analysis and explanation" (p. 97).

As with Greenander, Suppes obtains a probabilistic grammar by adding a conditional probability distribution on the set of productions. He defines a probabilistic *CF* grammar $G = (V_N, V_T, R, S, p)$ where, as usual, V_N is the set of non-terminals, V_T is the set of terminals, R is the set of production rules, S is the initial symbol, and, the additional parameter, p is a real-valued function defined on R such that:

(i)   for each $(\hat{\sigma i}, \sigma_j)$ in R, $P(\hat{\sigma i}, \sigma_j) \geqq 0$,
(ii)   for each $\hat{\sigma i}$ in the domain of R
$$\sum_{\sigma_j} P(\sigma_i, \sigma_j) = 1,$$

where the summation is over the range of R.

This means that for each set of production rules with the same left member σ_i, the sum of their probabilities is equal to 1, that is, probabilities are calculated for the set of re-writes for a given node $(= V_N)$.

What the Greenander and Suppes models fail to account for,

however, is dependency between rules. Both assume that choice is made only for re-write rules with the same left member. However, there would appear to be places in a performance grammar where the choice of one rule presupposes the previous choice of another rule. Examples include the choice of NP subject before object for a PS grammar, i.e., expansion of NP before VP.

A first attempt at accounting for some of this dependency appears in Salomaa (1969). In his paper Salomaa describes a class of grammars whose rewrite rules are restricted in some form. The grammar which he describes and formalizes in most detail is a probabilistic grammar. It is the purpose of the present section to describe and apply the concepts of the formal algebraic model developed by Salomaa to a non-probabilistic competence model proposed for a natural language (Rosenbaum 1967), but with probabilistic constraints conforming in format to Salomaa. In this way the native speaker's competence is still accounted for (i.e. in a sense all and only the sentences of the grammar are generated) but certain propensities for particular structures, etc., that is individual performance characteristics, can also be accounted for. The resultant probabilistic grammar is presented as a performance model rather than a competence model and interpretable in psychological, stylistic, social or other performance terms.

Let $G = \{V_N, V_T, S, F\}$ be the context free phrase structure grammar described in Rosenbaum (1967) where, in particular, $V_N = \{VP, NP, S\}$, $V_T = \{VB, N, T, \#\}$, $S \in V_N$ is the initial symbol and F is the set of core CF rewrite or production rules f_i. Following Salomaa let $G_P = \{G, \delta, \Phi\}$ where G is as above, δ is a stochastic vector representing the initial probability distribution of the rewrite rules, and Φ is a stochastic vector associated with each rewrite rule f whose i-th component indicates the probability that the i-th rewrite rule is applied after f. This then defines a probabilistic grammar G_P. To concretize these statements let us look at the actual rules posited for English by Rosenbaum:

$$S \rightarrow \# \; T \; NP \; VP \; \#$$

$$VP \rightarrow VB \; (NP) \; \left(\left\{ \begin{matrix} NP \\ S \end{matrix} \right\} \right)$$

$$NP \rightarrow \left\{ \begin{matrix} NP & S \\ N & (S) \end{matrix} \right\}$$

Inflating these rules in the usual way and putting them into Salomaa's format with probabilities stated for illustrative purposes only we obtain:

$f_1 : S \rightarrow \# \; T \; NP \; VP \; \#$ $(0 \;\; , .02, .08, .03, .06, .05, .16, .10, .50)$

$f_2 : VP \rightarrow VB$ $(0 \;\; , \; 0 \;\; , \; 0 \;\; , \; 0 \;\; , \; 0 \;\; , \; 0 \;\; , .18, .08, .74)$

$f_3 : VP \rightarrow VB \; NP$ $(0 \;\; , \; 0 \;\; , \; 0 \;\; , \; 0 \;\; , \; 0 \;\; , \; 0 \;\; , .16, .14, .70)$

$f_4 : VP \rightarrow VB \; NP \; NP$ $(0 \;\; , \; 0 \;\; , \; 0 \;\; , \; 0 \;\; , \; 0 \;\; , \; 0 \;\; , .14, .18, .68)$

$f_5 : VP \rightarrow VB \; NP \; S$ $(.10, \; 0 \;\; , \; 0 \;\; , \; 0 \;\; , \; 0 \;\; , \; 0 \;\; , .15, .16, .59)$

$f_6 : VP \rightarrow VB \; S$ $(.48, \; 0 \;\; , \; 0 \;\; , \; 0 \;\; , \; 0 \;\; , \; 0 \;\; , .12, .14, .26)$

$f_7 : NP \rightarrow NP \; S$ $(.18, .10, .08, .03, .05, .04, .10, .12, .30)$

$f_8 : NP \rightarrow N \; S$ $(.30, .16, .18, .12, .10, .14, \; 0 \;\; , \; 0 \;\; , \; 0 \;\;)$

$f_9 : NP \rightarrow N$ $(0 \;\; , .14, .36, .12, .18, .20, \; 0 \;\; , \; 0 \;\; , \; 0 \;\;)$

where the parenthesized expression in each rule f is the vector $\phi_i = (p_i^1, p_i^2, \ldots p_i^n)$ where p_i^j represents the probability of applying rule f_j after rule $f_i \cdot \sum_{i=1}^{n} p_i^n = 1$ and the initial probability distribution $\delta = (1, 0, 0, 0, 0, 0, 0, 0, 0)$.

For example the following trees might have been generated by applying rules f_1, f_2, and f_9 in the order described by the labels on the left.

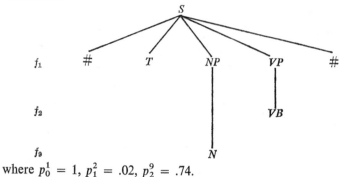

where $p_0^1 = 1$, $p_1^2 = .02$, $p_2^9 = .74$.

This tree is equivalent, except for order of application of the rules, to:

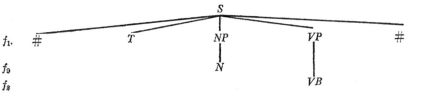

where $p_0^1 = 1$, $p_1^9 = .50$, $p_9^2 = .14$.

Both of these trees underlie the sentence of the language $L(G_P)$ $P = \# \ T \ N \ VB \ \#$. Their derivational histories can be represented by a CONTROL WORD. This is a record of the application of the re-write rules which takes the form of a left-to-right succession of the labels of the re-write rules applied in the derivation. There are two different control words for the two trees above (contrary to the usual interpretation of application in ordering of rules in a competence model, where order of expansion is irrelevant, cf. Bach 1964):

$$f_1 \qquad f_2 \qquad f_9$$

and

$$f_1 \qquad f_9 \qquad f_2$$

Let:

$$D: S_0 = P_0 \Rightarrow f_{j(1)} \ P_1 = f_{j(2)} \Rightarrow \ ... \ \Rightarrow f_{j(r)} \ P_r$$

be a derivation according to G_P where P_i now represents a line in the derivation and $f_{j(i+1)}$ is the label applied to the production going from P_i to P_{i+1}. Then for these two terminal strings:

$$D_1 : P_0 = S$$
$$P_1 = \# \ T \ NP \ VP \ \#$$
$$P_2 = \# \ T \ NP \ VB \ \#$$
$$P_3 = \# \ T \ N \ VB \ \#$$

and:

$$D_2 : P_0 = S$$
$$P_1 = \# \, T \, NP \, VP \, \#$$
$$P_2 = \# \, T \, N \, VP \, \#$$
$$P_3 = \# \, T \, N \, VB \, \#$$

we can define two different control words:

for $D_1 : f_{1(1)} \, f_{2(2)} \, f_{9(3)}$,
and for $D_2 : f_{1(1)} \, f_{9(2)} \, f_{2(3)}$.

These two derivations differ only in line P_2 which records the different order of expansion of NP or VP.

Although the order of application in a non-probabilistic grammar is irrevelant, it would be relevant for a performance grammar, for example, to represent time-dependent left-to-right stringing of words. If more weight should be given to generating a subject NP before a VP, then more weight should be given to the derivation D_2 than to D_1. We can characterize this notion by defining a function $\psi(D)$ – a measure of the probability of deriving a sentence as the weights of application differ. (This definition of $\psi(D)$ differs from Salomaa [but is similar to Greenander's $P(T)$] where length of derivation is used as a measure; this is because his function presupposes a grammar in a normal form where all rules are expansion rules into more than one symbol.) We can achieve this by considering $\psi(D)$ to be the product of the probabilities p_i^j of the rules used in constructing the derivation, a higher value for $\psi(D)$ being more desirable since a more probable derivation should be favored. In our examples above $\psi(D_1) = 1 \cdot .02 \cdot .74 = .0148$ and $\psi(D_2) = 1 \cdot .50 \cdot .14 = .0700$. Therefore $\psi(D_2) > \psi(D_1)$, that is, the propensity of choice of NP before VP can be built into the system.

This form of grammar thus can control the generation of the sentences by constraining rule application by means of a set of probabilities attached to each rule. In addition, it gives a way of measuring the probability of a particular sentence being derived.

I would like to demonstrate the usefulness of probabilistic

generative models not only as general performance models but also in one particular area of performance – that of literary stylistics. This exemplification will in turn show how the model can account for some aspects of individual style proposed by the well-known specialist in statistical stylistics Lubomir Doložel (in particular his proposal for a framework for statistical stylistics as described in Doležel 1969).

The statistical approach to style analysis considers style an intrinsic part of the theory of linguistic performance. Style is considered a probabilistic concept which describes not just a fixed norm and options, but accounts for the propensities for one or another of these options. What the model proposed above can account for in particular is two of the three shortcomings of performance models stated by Doležel (1969: 12).

(1) Performance schemes are strongly biased in the direction of representing the process of text recognition (i.e., the hearer's behavior) rather than the process of text production (the speaker's behavior). The style of a text, however, seems to be entirely a product of the speaker's behavior; variables that operate on the input of the process of communication seem to be responsible for the variety of styles. It can be assumed, therefore, that models of the "generation situation" will be much more relevant for the theory of style than will models of the "recognition situation".

(2) Because of their apragmatic nature, performance schemes usually lack a selectional component, that is, they do not provide a description of the processes that the speaker employs in selecting the one most appropriate mode of expression from a set of alternatives. It is well known from the history of stylistics that the notion of selection (choice) is crucial for many modern theories of style.

The model proposed here overcomes shortcoming (1) by describing the source, that is, it is a model of the text producing process (In actuality perhaps the goal of stylistic theory should be reformulated with this particular view in mind. If, as proposed by Turing, the goal of research in artificial intelligence is to create a machine which can fool a human into thinking that he is communicating with another human, then it seems reasonable to set the goal of a theory of style as the construction of a device which can write a novel in the style of a particular author.).

As for shortcoming (2) this model shows not only the possible choices in rule usage (that is the rules available) but in addition the particular probabilities of application as well.

In addition to the suggestions put forth by Doležel this model allows for an interesting theory of comparative stylistics. Namely, the generators can be compared rather than their respective texts. In particular this model can account for not only the presence vs. absence of a particular rule but also its differential usage. It can also make predictions about the occurrence of possible structures in the works of a particular author.

As an example of the descriptive power of the model to discriminate between two authors, we can reinterpret data from Hayes (1969) in his comparison of works by Gibbon and Hemingway. Hayes calculated the percentage of sentences having relative clause structures for the two authors as Gibbon 51 % and Hemingway 8 %. This information can be included in the proposed model by allowing every rule which feeds into the relative clause introducer (rule f_7: $NP \rightarrow NP\ S$) to contain the appropriate probability. For example, rules f_1 through f_7 can be followed by rule f_7 (that is, all but rules f_8 and f_9 can feed into f_7). The seventh component of the probability vector Φ associated with rules f_1 through f_7 would read .51 for Gibbon and .08 for Hemingway (with appropriate adjustment to the rest of the probabilities in each vector). For example, for the second rules in their respective grammars (if that term is appropriate for a performance model) we might have the following forms:

Gibbon: f_2 : $VP \rightarrow VB$
             (0, 0, 0, 0, 0, 0, .51, .245, .245)
Hemingway: f_2 : $VP \rightarrow VB$
             (0, 0, 0, 0, 0, 0, .08, .46, .46)

The difference between the two authors then shows up quite clearly.

Although quite revealing and conceptually interesting, this

model also suffers some inadequacies. One of the most crucial is an inadequacy of the competence model on which it is based, namely, a phrase structure grammar has memory limited to the preceding line in a derivation. There is no way of accounting therefore for such structures as sets of multiple embeddings or conjoinings – an obvious feature of performance which one would like to account for. It is difficult to see, however, how these can be accounted for, using the present scheme alone. I have suggested a somewhat more powerful model elsewhere (Smith forthcoming) which utilizes other types of constructs such as counters but I feel that these go beyond the scope of the present description. Futhermore, with changes in the description of competence models it may be that choice, which plays a crucial role in performance models, occurs high up in the grammar and that such constructs as particular transformations are completely predictable, triggered by the earlier higher choice. In any case, some of the tools for describing this choice within a formal probabilistic model are available and could be extended to these rules.

APPENDIX I

SAMPLE DESCRIPTIONS

A01 Press reportage: Spot news
A02 Press reportage: Financial
A03 Press reportage: Political
A04 Press reportage: Political
A05 Press reportage: Sports
A06 Press reportage: Sports
A07 Press reportage: Cultural
A08 Press reportage: Spot news
A09 Press reportage: Spot news
B01 Personal editorials
B02 Institutional editorial
B03 Letters to editor
B04 Letters to editor
B05 Personal editorials
B06 Institutional editorials
C01 Visual art reviews
D01 Book on the Russian church
D02 Article on the 17th century church
D03 Book on church holydays
D04 Book on atheism
D05 Article in collection
E01 Magazine articles
E02 Magazine articles
E03 Magazine articles
E04 Magazine articles
E05 Magazine articles
E06 Book on chess

F01 Magazine articles
F02 Magazine articles
F03 Magazine articles
F04 Magazine article
F05 Book on the dance
F06 History of the circus
F07 Book on the future
G01 Book, Memoirs (Ehrenburg)
G02 Article, Memoirs (B. Izakov)
G03 Article, Memoirs (L. Lazarev)
G04 Biography
G05 Belles Lettres
G06 Speech (Khrushchev)
G07 Memoirs (A. Dralkič)
G08 Belles Lettres
G09 Memoirs (S. Maršak)
G10 Memoirs (V. Panova)
G11 Memoirs (Ju. Oleša)
G12 Memoirs (M. Šoloxov)
G13 Memoirs (V. Poltorackij)
G14 Memoirs (M. Slonimskij)
G15 Speech on agricultural production
G16 Memoirs (V. Nikolaeva-Tereškova)
H01 Laws establishing courts
H02 Agricultural manual
H03 Text of a treaty
H04 College catalogue
H05 Agricultural manual
J01 Literary criticism
J02 History of Russian literature
J03 Political study
J04 Art history
J05 Soviet music
J06 Peasant wars
J07 Russian-English relations
J08 Political study
J09 Negro

J10 History of agriculture
J11 International law
J12 Geography
J13 Education
J14 Anthropology
J15 Sociology
K01 Novel (Ju. Libedinskij)
K02 Short story (V. Lipatov)
K03 Short story (S. Antonov)
K04 Novel (Ju. Bondarev)
K05 Novel (A. Antonovič)
K06 Novel (V. Ketlinskaja)
K07 Novel (V. Lidin)
K08 Novel (V. Kočetov)
K09 Novel (V. Koževnikov)
K10 Novel (A. Solženicyn)
K11 Novel (Ju. Kazakov)
K12 Novel (V. Tendrjakov)
K13 Novel (V. Solouxin)
K14 Novel (V. Dudincev)
L01 Children's fairy tale
N01 Adventure novel (S. Babaevskij)
N02 Adventure short story (N. Gribačev)
N03 Adventure novel (N. Zadornov)
N04 Adventure novel (Ju. Trifonov)
N05 Adventure novel (S. Sartakov)
N06 Adventure novel (N. Virta)
P01 Historical novel (D. Bregova)
P02 Historical novel (K. Paustovskij)
P03 Historical novel (N. Kazakov)
P04 Historical novel (K. Simonov)
P05 Historical novel (S. Zlobin)
P06 Historical novel (M. Šaginjan)
P07 Historical novel (B. D'jakov)
P08 Historical novel (A. Sokolov)
R01 Humor

APPENDIX II

RUSSIAN CORPUS STATISTICS

Sample	Types V	Tokens N	V/N	Log V/Log N	E	L
A01	1351	2026	.6668	.9467	.9388	.8888
A02	1214	2008	.6045	.9338	.9286	.8671
A03	1133	2001	.5662	.9251	.9263	.8570
A04	1196	2007	.5959	.9319	.9244	.8615
A05	1378	2166	.6361	.9411	.9343	.8793
A06	1208	1963	.6153	.9359	.9432	.8828
A07	1147	1997	.5743	.9270	.9114	.8449
A08	1251	2005	.6239	.9379	.9317	.8739
A09	1334	2108	.6328	.9402	.9331	.8773
B01	1217	1998	.6091	.9347	.9272	.8667
B02	779	1991	.3912	.8764	.8756	.7675
B03	1204	2013	.5981	.9324	.9339	.8708
B04	1177	2060	.5713	.9266	.9225	.8548
B05	1169	1997	.5853	.9295	.9246	.8595
B06	1259	2000	.6295	.9391	.9334	.8765
C01	1287	2012	.6396	.9412	.9301	.8755
D01	1252	1998	.6266	.9384	.9270	.8700
D02	1046	2010	.5203	.9141	.9119	.8336
D03	1002	1984	.5050	.9100	.9104	.8285
D04	1167	1948	.5990	.9323	.9218	.8594
D05	1048	2022	.5182	.9136	.9180	.8387
E01	1231	2015	.6109	.9352	.9323	.8719
E02	1272	2014	.6315	.9395	.9307	.8745
E03	1194	2010	.5940	.9315	.9245	.8612
E04	1197	1996	.5996	.9327	.9258	.8635
E05	1085	1943	.5584	.9230	.9208	.8500
E06	1127	2002	.5629	.9244	.9091	.8404
F01	1221	2003	.6095	.9348	.9279	.8675
F02	1345	2028	.6632	.9460	.9356	.8851
F03	1184	2008	.5896	.9305	.9162	.8525
F04	1087	1994	.5451	.9201	.9200	.8466
F05	1312	2105	.6232	.9382	.9197	.8628

Sample	Types V	Tokens N	V/N	Log V/Log N	E	L
F06	1124	2001	.5617	.9241	.9054	.8367
F07	1155	2024	.5706	.9263	.9260	.8577
G01	1201	2015	.5960	.9319	.9255	.8626
G02	1237	2028	.6099	.9350	.9231	.8632
G03	1203	2042	.5891	.9305	.9173	.8537
G04	1199	2000	.5995	.9326	.9202	.8583
G05	1171	2041	.5737	.9271	.9169	.8500
G06	1166	2015	.5786	.9281	.9257	.8591
G07	1135	2023	.5610	.9240	.9218	.8518
G08	1184	2018	.5867	.9299	.9146	.8505
G09	1113	2003	.5556	.9227	.9023	.8325
G10	1147	1993	.5755	.9272	.9140	.8475
G11	1245	2191	.5682	.9265	.9179	.8504
G12	1120	1981	.5653	.9248	.9109	.8425
G13	1236	2008	.6155	.9361	.9266	.8675
G14	1136	2052	.5536	.9224	.9119	.8412
G15	989	2093	.4725	.9019	.8960	.8081
G16	1237	2020	.6123	.9355	.9202	.8609
H01	633	2022	.3130	.8474	.8748	.7413
H02	716	2008	.3565	.8644	.8869	.7666
H03	755	2036	.3708	.8697	.8759	.7619
H04	355	2001	.1774	.7725	.8266	.6385
H05	854	1980	.4313	.8892	.8917	.7929
J01	1137	2047	.5554	.9228	.9099	.8397
J02	1133	1889	.5997	.9322	.9204	.8580
J03	1030	1996	.5160	.9129	.9197	.8397
J04	1027	1993	.5153	.9127	.9081	.8288
J05	1251	2009	.6226	.9377	.9373	.8789
J06	1123	2021	.5556	.9228	.9210	.8499
J07	1076	1982	.5428	.9195	.9131	.8396
J08	1107	1997	.5543	.9223	.9182	.8469
J09	1026	1967	.5216	.9141	.9102	.8321
J10	1023	2034	.5029	.9097	.9113	.8291
J11	1013	2009	.5042	.9099	.9126	.8305
J12	1006	1999	.5032	.9096	.9145	.8319
J13	1085	2003	.5416	.9193	.9074	.8342
J14	1017	2008	.5064	.9105	.9253	.8426
J15	1080	2057	.5250	.9155	.9191	.8415
K01	1270	2014	.6305	.9393	.9307	.8743
K02	1043	2005	.5201	.9140	.9098	.8316
K03	1059	1981	.5345	.9175	.9016	.8272
K04	1134	1996	.5681	.9255	.9236	.8549
K05	1244	1974	.6301	.9391	.9347	.8778
K06	1093	1949	.5608	.9236	.9148	.8449
K07	1223	2116	.5779	.9284	.9010	.8365

Sample	Types V	Tokens N	V/N	Log V/Log N	E	L
K08	1256	2033	.6178	.9367	.9244	.8659
K09	1265	2027	.6240	.9380	.9305	.8729
K10	1122	2015	.5568	.9230	.9098	.8398
K11	1122	2013	.5573	.9231	.9115	.8415
K12	1273	1983	.6419	.9416	.9294	.8751
K13	1167	1974	.5911	.9307	.9205	.8567
K14	1065	2000	.5325	.9170	.9083	.8330
L01	1207	1983	.6086	.9346	.9238	.8634
N01	1131	2143	.5277	.9166	.8913	.8171
N02	1171	2004	.5843	.9293	.9073	.8432
N03	1163	1973	.5894	.9303	.9146	.8509
N04	1060	1951	.5433	.9194	.9100	.8367
N05	1088	1916	.5678	.9251	.9187	.8499
N06	1250	2006	.6231	.9377	.9244	.8669
P01	1124	2009	.5594	.9236	.9065	.8372
P02	1166	2012	.5795	.9282	.9150	.8494
P03	1232	1964	.6272	.9384	.9289	.8717
P04	1169	2027	.5767	.9277	.9206	.8540
P05	1186	1996	.5941	.9314	.9145	.8518
P06	1162	2016	.5763	.9275	.9131	.8470
P07	1257	1987	.6326	.9397	.9260	.8702
P08	1218	2009	.6062	.9342	.9232	.8625
R01	1248	2075	.6014	.9334	.9167	.8556

APPENDIX III

SAMPLES RANKED FOR *L* BY GENRE[a]

RANK	GENRE													
	A	B	C	D	E	F	G	H	J	K	L	N	P	R
1	01													
2						02								
3	06													
4	05													
5									05					
6										05				
7	09													
8		06												
9			01											
10										12				
11					02									
12										01				
13	08													
14										09				
15					01									
16													03	
17		03												
18													07	
19				01										
20							13							
21						01								
22	02													
23												06		
24		01												
25										08				
26					04									
27											01			
28							02							
29						05								

[a] The two-digit number refers to the particular sample.

Rank	Genre													
	A	B	C	D	E	F	G	H	J	K	L	N	P	R
30							01							
31													08	
32	04													
33					03									
34							16							
35		05												
36				04										
37							06							
38							04							
39									02					
40						07								
41	03													
42										13				
43														01
44										04				
45		04												
46													04	
47							03							
48						03								
49													05	
50							07							
51												03		
52							08							
53							11							
54							05							
55					05									
56												05		
57									06					
58													02	
59							10							
60													06	
61									08					
62						04								
63									06					
64	07													
65												02		
66								14						
67						12								
68								15						
69									11					
70						14								
71				06										
72										10				

Rank	Genre													
	A	B	C	D	E	F	G	H	J	K	L	N	P	R
73									01					
74									03					
75									07					
76				05										
77													01	
78												04		
79						06								
80										07				
81									13					
82				02										
83										14				
84							09							
85									09					
86									12					
87										02				
88									11					
89									10					
90									04					
91				03										
92										03				
93												01		
94							15							
95								05						
96		02												
97							02							
98							03							
99							01							
100							04							

APPENDIX IV

LIST OF FUNCTION WORDS

a	kak	pod
bez	ko	počemu
bliz	kogda	posle
daby	krome	prežde
dlja	kuda	pri
do	li	pro
esli	meždu	protiv
gde	mimo	s
čem	na	skvoz'
čerez	nad	so
čto	no	sredi
čtob	o	u
čtoby	ob	v
i	obo	vne
ibo	okolo	vo
ili	ot	xotja
iz	oto	xot'
iz-pod	pered	za
iz-za	peredo	začem
k	po	jakoby

REFERENCES

Bach, E.
1964 *An introduction to transformational grammars* (New York).
Chomsky, N.
1956 "Three models for the description of language", *I.R.E. Transactions on Information Theory*, IT-2: 113-124.
1958 Review of V. Belevitch, *Langage des machines et langage humain*, *Language* 34: 99-105.
1963 "Formal properties of grammers", in: *Handbook of mathematical psychology* II, ed. by R. D. Luce, R. R. Bush, and E. Galanter: 323-418 (New York).
1965 *Aspects of the theory of syntax* (Cambridge, Mass.).
Chomsky, N. and M. Halle
1968 *Sound pattern of English* (New York).
Doležel, L.
1967 "The Prague School and the statistical theory of poetic language", in: *Prague studies in mathematical linguistics* II: 97-104 (Prague).
1969 "A framework for the statistical analysis of style", in: *Statistics and style*, ed. by L. Doležel and R. W. Bailey: 10-25 (New York).
Fodor, J. and M. Garrett
1966 "Some reflections on competence and performance", in: *Psycholinguistics papers*, ed. by J. Lyons and R. J. Wales: 133-154 (Edinburgh).
Fromkin, V.
1971 "The non-anomalous nature of anomalous utterances", *Language* 47: 25-52.
Greenander, U.
1967 *Syntax-controlled probabilities* (Brown University, Division of Applied Mathematics).
Guiraud, P.
1959 *Problèmes et méthodes de la statistique linguistique* (Dordrecht).
Hass, W.
1970 "Properties of information-theory measures of grammatical goodness-of-fit", in: *Proceedings of the Conference on Linguistics*: 110-117 (The University of Iowa).
Halle, M.
1958 Review of G. Herdan, *Language as choice and chance*, *Kratylos* 3: 20-28.

Halle, M. and K. Stevens
1964 "Speech recognition: a model and a program for research", in: *The structure of language*, ed. by J. Fodor and J. Katz: 604-612 (Englewood Cliffs).

Halliday, M. A. K.
1970 "Language structure and language function", in *New horizons in linguistics*, ed. by J. Lyons: 140-165 (Baltimore).

Hayes, C.
1969 "A study in prose styles: Edward Gibbon and Ernest Hemingway", reprinted in: *Statistics and style*, ed. by L. Doležel and R. W. Bailey: 80-94 (New York).

Herdan, G.
1960 *Type-token mathematics* (The Hague).

Hockett, C.
1955 *A manual of phonology*, International Journal of American Linguistics Memoir 11.
1961 "Grammar for the hearer", in: *Proceedings of symposia in applied mathematics* XII: 220-236 (Providence).

Josselson, H.
1953 *The Russian word count* (Detroit).

Kay, M.
1970 *Performance grammars* (The RAND Corporation, Santa Monica).

Kučera, H.
1968 "Some quantitative lexical analyses of Russian, Czech, and English", in: *American contributions to the Sixth International Congress of Slavists* I: 1-44 (The Hague).

Kučera, H. and W. N. Francis
1967 *A computational analysis of present-day edited American English* (Providence).

Kučera, H. and G. Monroe
1968 *A comparative quantitative phonology of Russian, Czech, and German* (New York).

Labov, W.
1971 "Methodology", in: *A survey of linguistic science*, ed. by W. O. Dingwall (University of Maryland, Program in Linguistics).

Lees, R.
1959 Review of L. Apostel, B. Mandelbrot, and A. Morf, *Logique, Langage et theorie de l'information*, Language 35: 271-303.

Leont'ev, A. A.
1969 *Psixolingvisticeskie edinicy i poroždenie recevogo vyskazyvanija* (Moscow).

Mandelbrot, B.
1961 "On the theory of word frequencies and on related Markovian models of discourse", *Proceedings of symposia in applied mathematics* XII: 190-219 (Providence).

Miller, G., and N. Chomsky
1963 "Finitary models of language users", in: *Handbook of mathematical*

psychology II, ed. by R. D. Luce, R. R. Bush, and E. Galanter: 421-464 (New York).

Oettinger, A.
  1960   *Automatic language translation* (Cambridge, Mass.).
Rosenbaum, P.
  1967   "English Grammar II", in: *Specification and utilization of a transformational grammar*, ed. by P. Rosenbaum: 667-800.
Saires, H.
  1956   *Cryptanalysis* (New York).
Salomaa, A.
  1969   "Probabilistic and weighted grammars", *Information and control* 15: 529-544.
Schwarz, R.
  1967   "Steps toward a model of linguistic performance: a preliminary sketch", *Mechanical translation* 10: 39-52.
Shannon, C. and W. Weaver
  1963   *The mathematical theory of communication* (Urbana).
Simon, H.
  1955   "On a class of skew distribution functions", *Biometrika* 42: 425-440.
Smith, R.
  forthcoming "Toward a representation scheme for performance", *Linguistics*.
Suppes, P.
  1970   "Probabilistic grammars for natural languages", *Synthese* 22: 95-116.
Wales, R. J. and J. C. Marshall
  1966   "The organization of linguistic performance", in: *Psycholinguistics papers*, ed. by J. Lyons and R. J. Wales: 27-80 (Edinburgh).
Weinreich, U.
  1966   "Explorations in semantic theory", in: *Current trends in linguistic theory* III, ed. by T. A. Sebeok: 395-477 (The Hague).
Whitaker, H.
  1971   "Neurolinguistics", in: *A survey of linguistic science*, ed. by W. O. Dingwall: 136-251 (University of Maryland, Program in Linguistics).
Yule, G.
  1944   *The statistical study of literary vocabulary* (Cambridge, England).
Zipf, G.
  1968   *The psycho-biology of language: an introduction to dynamic philology* (Cambridge, Mass.).